ADDISON-WESLEY

QUEST 2000

EXPLORING MATHEMATICS

Practice and Homework Book

AUTHORS
PEGGY MORROW AND ANNE BOYD

GRADE 2

Consulting Editor: Lesley Haynes
Editors: Fran Cohen, Brenda McLoughlin, Debbie
  Smith, First Folio Resource Group Inc.
Design, Art Direction, and Page Composition:
  Brian Lehen • Graphic Design Ltd.
Illustrators: Sami Suomalainen, Brian Lehen
Reviewer: Shirley Fairfield, Independent Consultant,
  North York, Ontario

Copyright © 1999 Pearson Education Canada Inc., Toronto, Ontario

This book contains recycled product and is acid free.
Printed and bound in Canada.

Addison
Wesley

Toronto

ISBN 0–201–43882–8

13 14 - WC - 08 07

CONTENTS

Practice and Homework Pages

Computation Skills Bank

To the Teacher

This *Practice and Homework Book* provides reinforcement of the concepts and skills explored in the *Quest 2000 Exploring Mathematics* program.

There are two sections in the book. The first section follows the sequence of *Quest 2000 Exploring Mathematics*. It is intended for use throughout the year as you are teaching the program's eleven units and the Core Activities described in the *Teacher's Guide & Journal*. A two-page spread supports the content of each Core Activity within the units.

The two-page spread is linked to a unit activity.

The title identifies the learning outcome of the activity. ⟍

The left page is the "practice" page and is intended for classroom use following completion of the Core Activity. ⟶

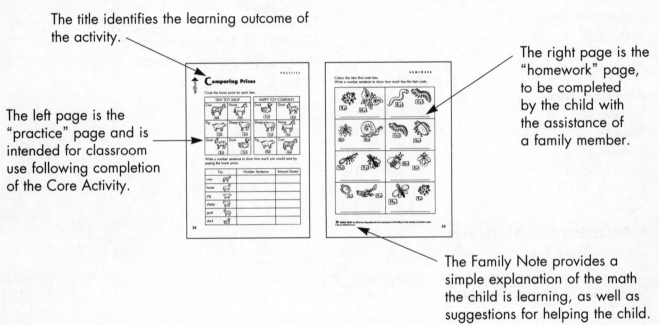

The right page is the "homework" page, to be completed by the child with the assistance of a family member.

The Family Note provides a simple explanation of the math the child is learning, as well as suggestions for helping the child.

The second section of the book is a *Computation Skills Bank* — a series of pages that you can use at any time to develop and maintain students' facility with basic facts and proficiency with computational skills. These pages provide ongoing practice and can be used in class or assigned as homework. The strategies pages help students use thinking strategies to derive the answers to the facts. Additional practice pages, which can be used as either class work or homework, can be found in the *Extra Practice and Testing Masters* component of the *Quest 2000 Exploring Mathematics* program.

To the Family

The homework pages in this book will help your child practise the mathematical skills and concepts that he or she is exploring at school. As you assist your child to complete each page, you will have an opportunity to become involved in your child's learning.

The homework page is always on the right page of a two-page spread and is closely linked to the content of the left page, which your child will have completed in class.

A Family Note at the bottom of each homework page explains the math your child is learning, and suggests some of the ways you can assist your child. Here are more ways to help:

• Read the instructions on the page with or for your child to make sure she or he understands what to do.

• Encourage your child to explain his or her thinking during the completion of the page.

• Many of the pages require small objects for counting and for measuring. Gather items such as buttons, toothpicks, pennies, small stones, and coloured yarn. It would also be helpful to provide a ruler and measuring tape marked in centimetres.

These homework pages are intended to be enjoyable for you and your child, as well as to help your child improve his or her mathematics skills. Perhaps as you work through the book together, you will have other ideas for math activities that your child can share with the rest of the class.

This math workbook will be sent home frequently throughout the year. Please help your child complete the assigned page. Make sure the book is returned promptly, since it is to be used at school as well as at home.

Sorting People

How have the children been sorted?
Draw a picture of another child in each group.
Write the sorting rule.

Sorting Rule: _____

_____

Sort your friends or family members into two groups.
Draw pictures.
Write your sorting rule.

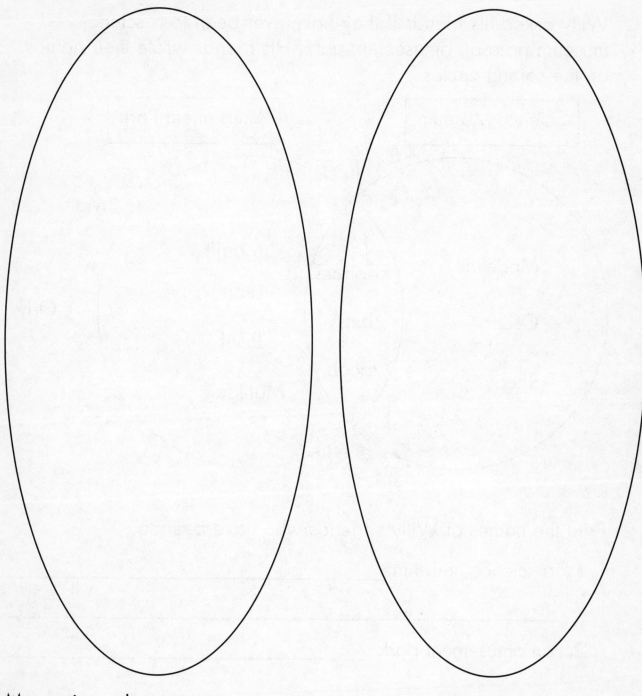

My sorting rule: _____

_____

_____

🏠 **FAMILY NOTE:** Your child is learning that people can be sorted and re-sorted into groups based on their similarities and differences. After your child completes this page, ask him or her to think of another way to sort the people.

Using Sorting Circles

Willy asked his friends if they have ever been to a science museum or to an amusement park. His friends wrote their names on the sorting circles.

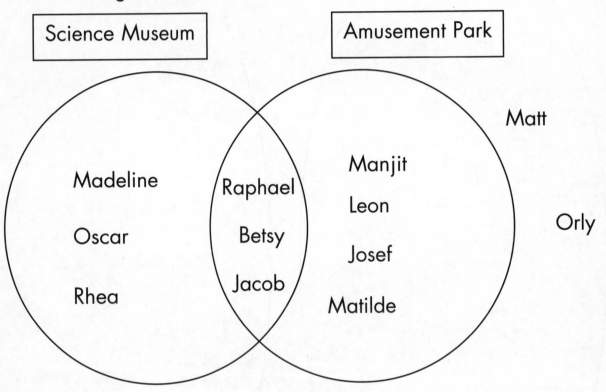

Science Museum | Amusement Park

Madeline

Oscar

Rhea

Raphael

Betsy

Jacob

Manjit

Leon

Josef

Matilde

Matt

Orly

Print the names of Willy's friends who have been to:

1. a science museum _____

_____

2. an amusement park _____

_____

3. both places _____

_____

4. neither place _____

_____

4

Ask some people at home the question.
Have them write their names on the sorting circles.

Do you have a bicycle or in-line skates?

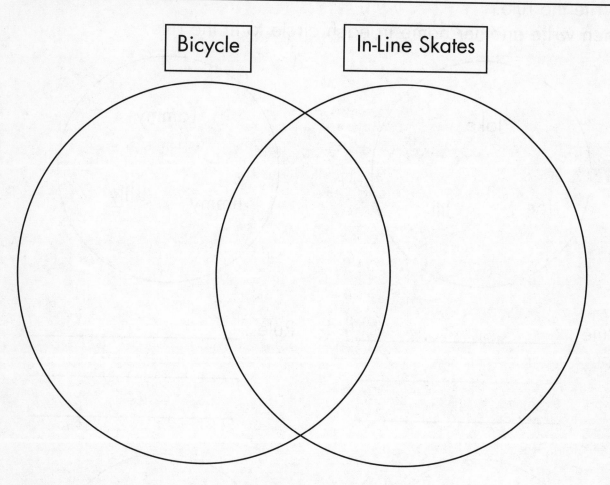

Bicycle

In-Line Skates

Write what the sorting circles show.

_____

_____

_____

_____

_____

_____

🏠 **FAMILY NOTE:** Your child is learning to use intersecting circles to show that people can be classified in more than one group at a time. Ask questions such as, "How many people have a bicycle but not in-line skates?", "How many people have both?", and "How many have neither?"

Sorting Names

Guess the sorting rule for each group of names.
Write the rule.
Then write another name in each circle to fit the rule.

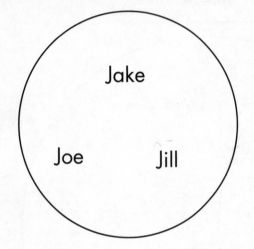

Jake

Joe   Jill

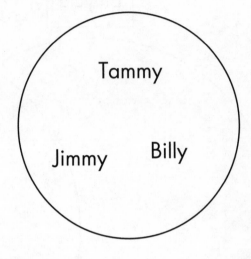

Tammy

Jimmy   Billy

Rule : _____

_____

_____

Rule : _____

_____

_____

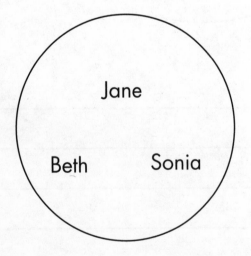

Jane

Beth   Sonia

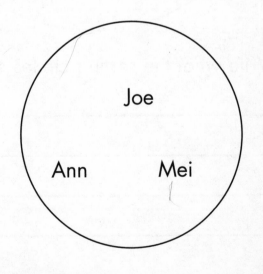

Joe

Ann   Mei

Rule : _____

_____

_____

Rule : _____

_____

_____

Write the names of ten people you know.
Then choose some names that are alike.
Write the names in the circle.
Write the rule.

Names

_____ _____

_____ _____

_____ _____

_____ _____

_____ _____

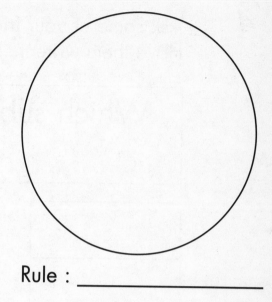

Rule : _____

_____

_____

Now sort the names to make two more groups.
Write the names in each circle.
Write the rules.

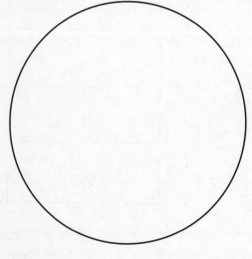

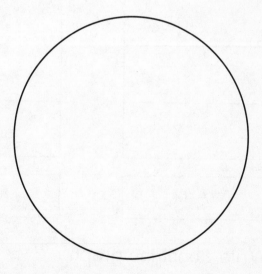

Rule : _____   Rule : _____

_____   _____

_____   _____

🏠 **FAMILY NOTE:** Your child is learning to sort and re-sort names to form groups. Remind your child that each group needs to contain only a few names, that some names may appear in more than one group, and that not all the names need to be used.

Making a Name Graph

Ask some of your friends the question.
Have them write their names on the graph.

Which subject do you like best — art, music, or gym?

Art	Music	Gym

Write about the graph.

_____

_____

_____

Ask some people at home the question.
Have them write their names on the graph.

What kind of potatoes do you like best?

mashed				

French fries				

roasted				

pan-fried				

boiled				

Write about the graph.

_____

_____

_____

_____

_____

FAMILY NOTE: Your child has been collecting data to create name graphs. Help your child interpret the graph by asking questions such as, "Which kind of potatoes do more people prefer?," "How many more people like _____ than _____?," and "How many people like either French fries or mashed potatoes?"

UNIT
1
ACTIVITY
5

Making Picture Graphs

Use string.
Measure the length of your arm.
Measure the arm lengths of five or six friends.
Draw pictures of your friends on the graph.

Comparing Arm Lengths

longer than my arm						

same length as my arm						

shorter than my arm						

Write about the graph.

_____

_____

_____

_____

Ask some people at home the question.
Draw a picture on the graph for each answer.

Which fruit do you like best — bananas, apples, oranges, or grapes?

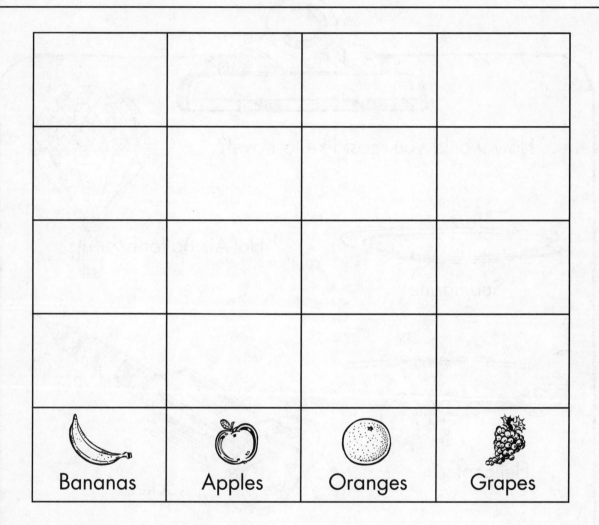

Bananas	Apples	Oranges	Grapes

Write about the graph.

_____

_____

_____

_____

UNIT
1
ACTIVITY
6

Taking Surveys

Ask some friends the question.
Use tally marks near the pictures to record the answers.

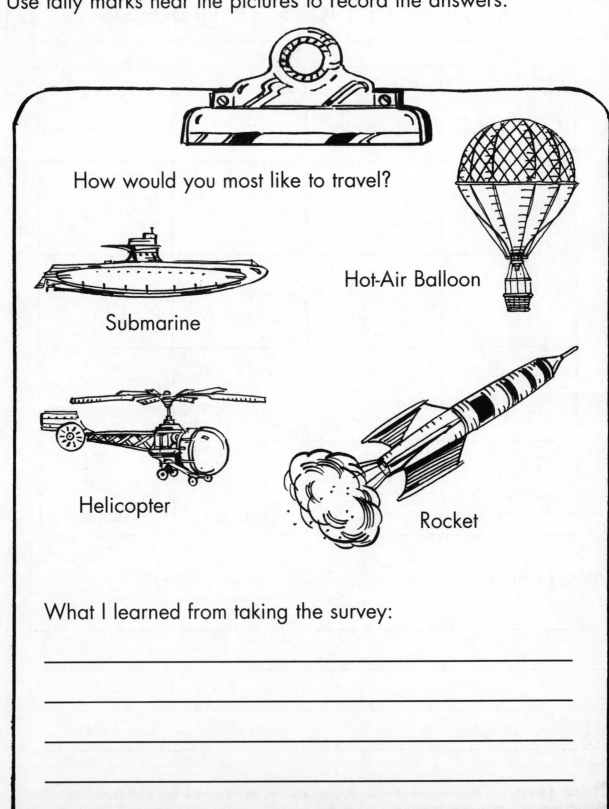

How would you most like to travel?

Submarine

Hot-Air Balloon

Helicopter

Rocket

What I learned from taking the survey:

_____

_____

_____

_____

Write a survey question of your own. Make sure your question has at least two choices.

Ask some people at home the question.
Use tally marks to record the answers.

Question: _____

_____

What I learned from taking the survey:

_____

_____

_____

FAMILY NOTE: Your child is learning to collect data by taking surveys, and to record data with tally marks. Help your child interpret the results of the survey by asking questions about the number of responses for each choice. For example, you might ask, "Which choice was least popular?", "How many people chose it?", and "How many more people chose _____ than _____?"

13

Displaying Data

Joel made a tally of the fireflies he counted in Cherry Park last week.

Monday	Tuesday	Wednesday	Thursday	Friday
IIII	卌 I	III	IIII	卌 II

Make a graph to show the data.
Give the graph a title.

_____

Ms. Cole's class voted to choose a name for their new pet
guinea pig.
The class made a tally of the votes.

Guinea Pig Names	
Muffin	|||
Fluffy	~~||||~~ ||
Zip	~~||||~~ ||
Scooter	~~||||~~ |||

Make a graph to show the data.
Give the graph a title.

_____

Write what the class found out.

_____

_____

_____

🏠 **FAMILY NOTE:** Your child is learning that data can be represented in many ways. As your child completes the graph, encourage him or her to label the rows.

15

Asking Questions

Here is some information collected by a Grade 2 class.
Write the question the children might have asked.

1.

bus	ⅢⅢ Ⅱ
walk	ⅢⅢ ⅢⅢ ⅢⅢ ⅢⅢ Ⅱ
bike	Ⅲ

_____

_____

_____

2.

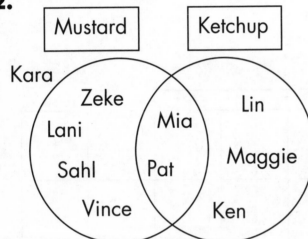

_____

_____

_____

3.

mushrooms							
pepperoni							
olives							
other							

_____

_____

_____

4.

size 1	👞 👞 👞 👞 👞 👞 👞
size 2	👞 👞 👞 👞 👞 👞 👞 👞
size 3	👞 👞 👞 👞 👞
size 4	👞

_____

_____

_____

16

Write a survey question you could ask each group.
Make sure each question has at least two choices.

1. teenagers

_____

_____

_____

2. kindergarten children

_____

_____

_____

3. teachers

_____

_____

_____

4. grown-ups

_____

_____

_____

5. people who like reading

_____

_____

_____

🏠 **FAMILY NOTE:** Your child is learning to formulate survey questions that could be used to collect data from groups of people. Help your child evaluate his or her questions and to revise them if necessary.

Telling Number Stories

Use counters on the story mat. Show each story.
Write a number sentence.

| 7 ladybugs are on the leaf.
5 more ladybugs join them.

_____ | 12 ladybugs are on the leaf.
8 ladybugs fly away.

_____ |

| 11 ladybugs are on the leaf.
4 ladybugs fly away.

_____ | 6 ladybugs are on the leaf.
4 more ladybugs join them.

_____ |

| 9 ladybugs are on the leaf.
2 more ladybugs join them.

_____ | 10 ladybugs are on the leaf.
7 ladybugs fly away.

_____ |

Create a story to match each number sentence.
Use pictures or words.

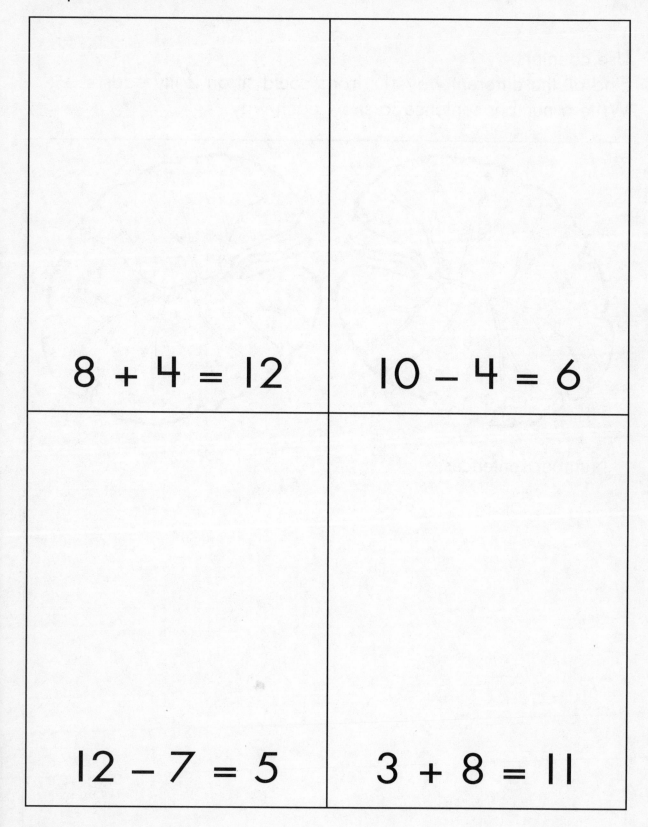

8 + 4 = 12

10 − 4 = 6

12 − 7 = 5

3 + 8 = 11

FAMILY NOTE: Your child has been making up addition and subtraction stories. She or he may wish to act out each story with small counters, such as pennies or buttons, before drawing or writing.

19

UNIT
2
ACTIVITY
2

Finding Number Combinations

Use counters.
Find all the different ways 12 frogs could sit on 2 lily pads.
Write a number sentence to show each way.

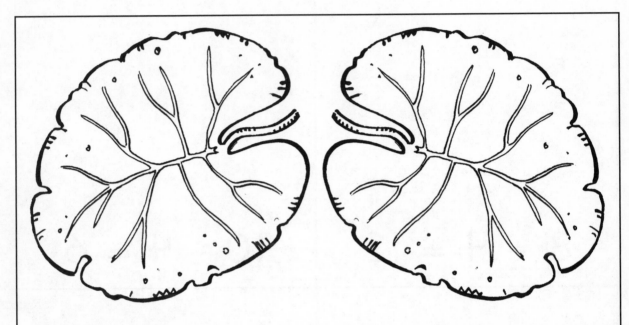

Number sentences:

Use counters.
Find different ways 12 people could sit on 3 benches.
Write a number sentence to show each way.

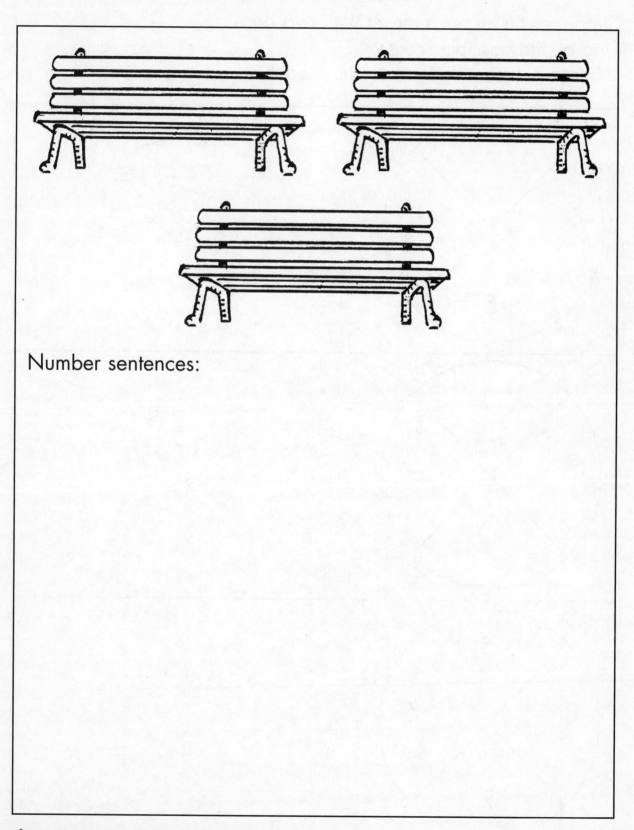

Number sentences:

Finding All the Possible Totals (1)

Suppose you hit each target with two darts.
Find all the possible scores.
Write a number sentence to show each score.

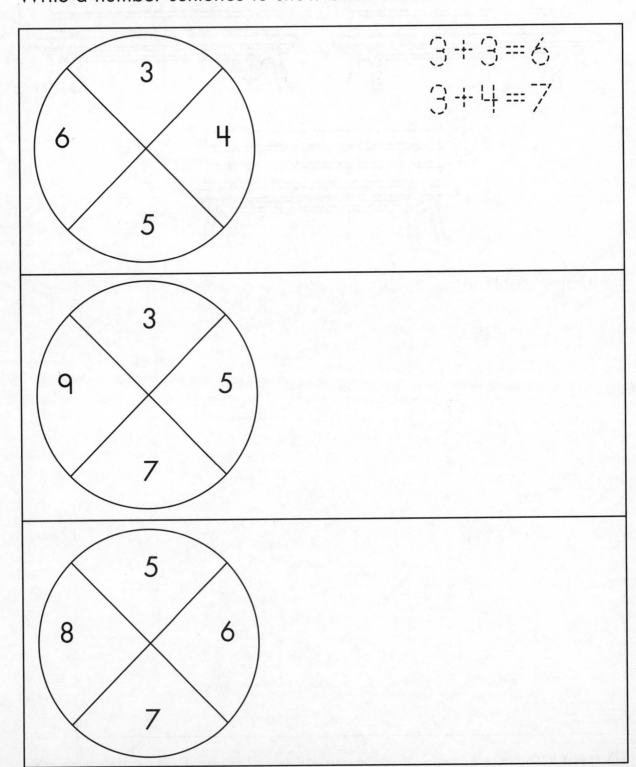

Write your own numbers on each target.
Suppose you hit each target with two darts.
Find all the possible scores.
Write a number sentence to show each score.

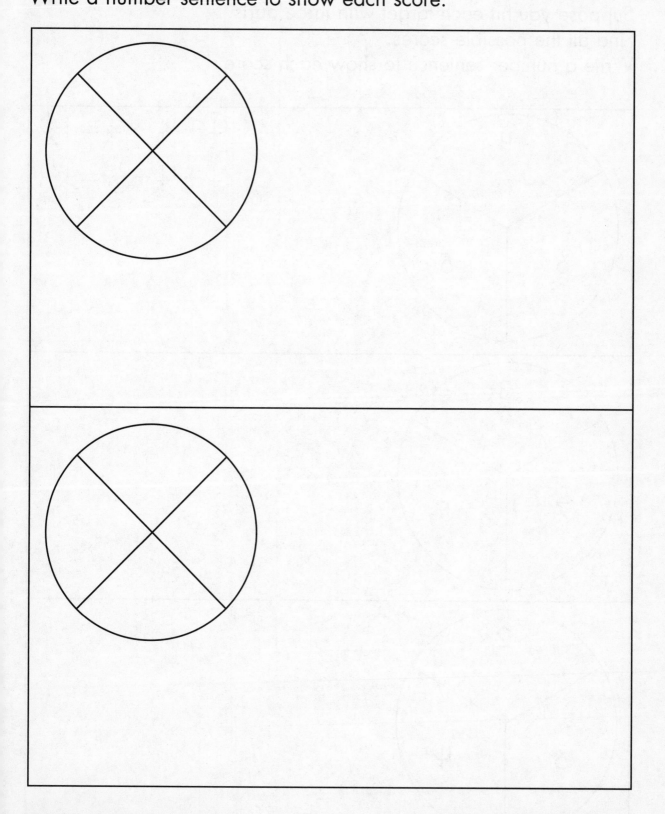

🏠 **FAMILY NOTE:** Your child has been looking for all the different point combinations and scores that are possible in a game. This helps your child recognize that different numbers can combine to form the same total.

Finding All the Possible Totals (2)

Suppose you hit each target with three darts.
Find all the possible scores.
Write a number sentence to show each score.

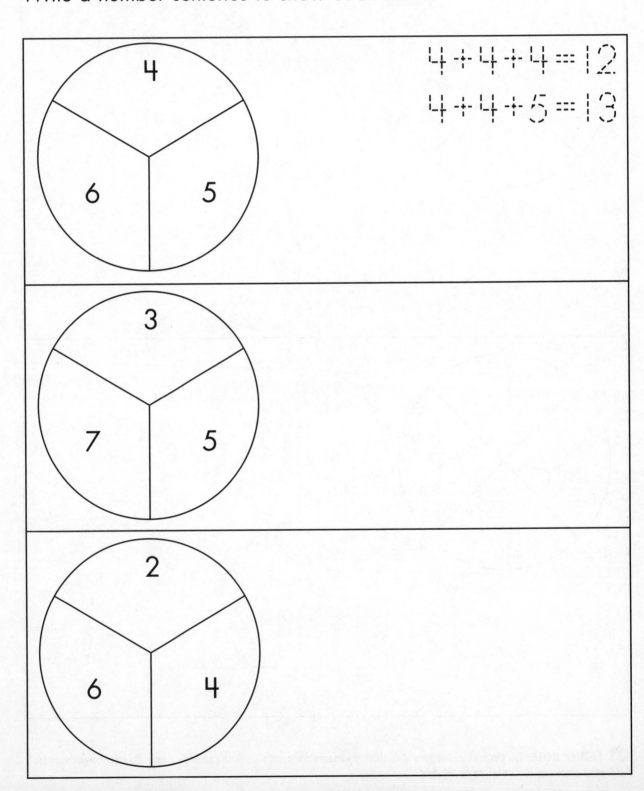

4 + 4 + 4 = 12
4 + 4 + 5 = 13

Write your own numbers on the target.
Suppose you hit the target with three darts.
Find all the possible scores.
Write a number sentence to show each score.

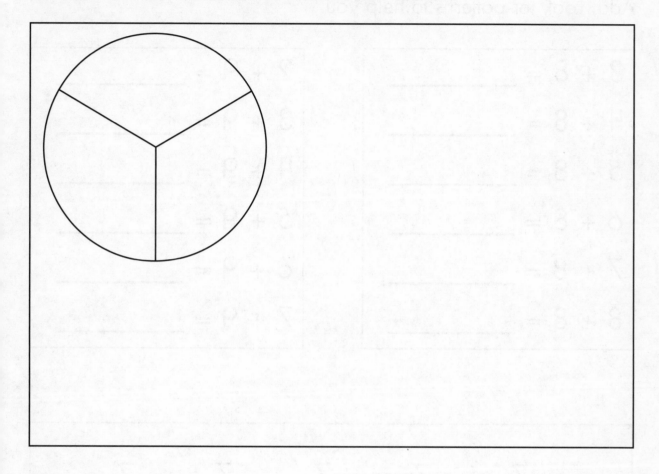

Add.

6 + 3 + 5 = _____   1 + 7 + 6 = _____

3 + 4 + 8 = _____   5 + 2 + 4 = _____

7 + 2 + 9 = _____   3 + 5 + 4 = _____

$$
\begin{array}{r} 2 \\ 4 \\ +7 \\ \hline \end{array}
\qquad
\begin{array}{r} 3 \\ 7 \\ +4 \\ \hline \end{array}
\qquad
\begin{array}{r} 5 \\ 5 \\ +6 \\ \hline \end{array}
\qquad
\begin{array}{r} 4 \\ 5 \\ +6 \\ \hline \end{array}
\qquad
\begin{array}{r} 3 \\ 1 \\ +8 \\ \hline \end{array}
\qquad
\begin{array}{r} 6 \\ 5 \\ +2 \\ \hline \end{array}
$$

Finding Patterns in Addition

Add. Look for patterns to help you.

3 + 8 = _____	2 + 9 = _____
4 + 8 = _____	3 + 9 = _____
5 + 8 = _____	4 + 9 = _____
6 + 8 = _____	5 + 9 = _____
7 + 8 = _____	6 + 9 = _____
8 + 8 = _____	7 + 9 = _____

$$\begin{array}{r} 7 \\ +\ 3 \\ \hline \end{array} \qquad \begin{array}{r} 7 \\ +\ 4 \\ \hline \end{array} \qquad \begin{array}{r} 7 \\ +\ 5 \\ \hline \end{array} \qquad \begin{array}{r} 7 \\ +\ 6 \\ \hline \end{array} \qquad \begin{array}{r} 7 \\ +\ 7 \\ \hline \end{array}$$

$$\begin{array}{r} 5 \\ +\ 5 \\ \hline \end{array} \qquad \begin{array}{r} 5 \\ +\ 6 \\ \hline \end{array} \qquad \begin{array}{r} 5 \\ +\ 7 \\ \hline \end{array} \qquad \begin{array}{r} 5 \\ +\ 8 \\ \hline \end{array} \qquad \begin{array}{r} 5 \\ +\ 9 \\ \hline \end{array}$$

Add. Look for patterns to help you.

5	6	7	8	9
+ 6	+ 6	+ 6	+ 6	+ 6

4	5	6	7	8
+ 9	+ 9	+ 9	+ 9	+ 9

5	6	7	8	9
+ 7	+ 7	+ 7	+ 7	+ 7

6 + 4 = _____

6 + 5 = _____

6 + 6 = _____

6 + 7 = _____

6 + 8 = _____

6 + 9 = _____

4 + 4 = _____

4 + 5 = _____

4 + 6 = _____

4 + 7 = _____

4 + 8 = _____

4 + 9 = _____

FAMILY NOTE: Your child has been working with addition facts with sums to 18. Ask your child to describe the patterns in the rows and columns of facts on this page.

Using an Addition Table

Complete the addition table.
Use patterns to help you.

+	1	2	3	4	5	6	7	8	9
1	2	3	4					9	
2		4		6			9		
3	4				8				12
4		6	7			10		12	
5	6				10			13	
6		8				12			
7		9			12				16
8			11				15		
9		11			14			17	

Colour six sums in the addition table.
Write the addition sentence for each sum.

_____   _____

_____   _____

Add.
Use the addition table on page 28 to help you.

4 + 5 = _____   5 + 2 = _____   9 + 5 = _____

6 + 7 = _____   9 + 9 = _____   3 + 9 = _____

2 + 8 = _____   7 + 9 = _____   7 + 4 = _____

9 + 8 = _____   8 + 3 = _____   6 + 9 = _____

8 + 8 = _____   4 + 9 = _____   3 + 7 = _____

6 + 8 = _____   5 + 5 = _____   5 + 7 = _____

9	3	9	4	5	8
+7	+4	+2	+8	+6	+9

7	4	5	7	3	6
+7	+6	+3	+8	+6	+5

8	5	6	4	8	6
+7	+8	+4	+2	+6	+6

FAMILY NOTE: Help your child locate the answers to the facts on this page by using the addition table on page 28. For example, to find the answer to 4 + 5, find the 4 along the left side of the grid, then count over five spaces.

29

UNIT
2
ACTIVITY
7

Using Rules

Write a rule to get from the first number to the second number.

First Number	Second Number
18	9
17	8
16	7
15	6
14	5

Rule: _____

First Number	Second Number
5	13
6	14
7	15
8	16
9	17

Rule: _____

First Number	Second Number
8	14
5	11
3	9
7	13
6	12

Rule: _____

First Number	Second Number
12	5
14	7
10	3
16	9
11	4

Rule: _____

Write a rule.
Make a list of first numbers for your rule.
Then use your rule to write the second numbers.

Rule: _____

First Number	Second Number

Rule: _____

First Number	Second Number

Rule: _____

First Number	Second Number

Rule: _____

First Number	Second Number

FAMILY NOTE: Each rule your child writes should use either addition or subtraction. Your child will use the rule to determine the second number in each set. For example, if the rule is "add 5" and the first numbers are 6, 7, 8, 9, and 10, then the resulting second numbers will be 11, 12, 13, 14, and 15.

Using Strategies to Add and Subtract

Find each sum using any strategy you wish.

7 + 5 = _____   2 + 9 = _____   7 + 9 = _____

7 + 6 = _____   5 + 9 = _____   6 + 8 = _____

8 + 4 = _____   9 + 9 = _____   8 + 5 = _____

9 + 8 = _____   7 + 8 = _____   8 + 6 = _____

9 + 6 = _____   6 + 7 = _____   3 + 8 = _____

7 + 5 = _____   9 + 5 = _____   9 + 4 = _____

5	9	4	8	8	9
+9	+6	+8	+9	+5	+7

9	8	6	9	4	8
+3	+8	+9	+4	+7	+7

Choose one strategy you used. Write about it.

_____

_____

_____

Find each difference using any strategy you wish.

16 – 8 = _____   12 – 3 = _____   15 – 6 = _____

14 – 6 = _____   18 – 9 = _____   14 – 9 = _____

13 – 5 = _____   15 – 8 = _____   17 – 8 = _____

12 – 4 = _____   14 – 7 = _____   13 – 8 = _____

17 – 9 = _____   12 – 6 = _____   15 – 9 = _____

12 – 8 = _____   13 – 9 = _____   11 – 4 = _____

10	15	14	12	13	16
– 6	– 7	– 8	– 5	– 4	– 7

13	11	12	16	13	14
– 6	– 8	– 7	– 9	– 7	– 5

Choose one strategy you used. Write about it.

_____

_____

_____

_____

FAMILY NOTE: Your child is learning to use strategies to find the answers to basic facts. Ask your child to explain some of the strategies to you.

Comparing Prices

Circle the lower price for each item.

TINY TOY SHOP	
Cow 16¢	Horse 14¢
Pig 7¢	Sheep 8¢
Goat 5¢	Duck 7¢

HAPPY TOY COMPANY	
Duck 4¢	Goat 10¢
Sheep 11¢	Horse 12¢
Pig 10¢	Cow 12¢

Write a number sentence to show how much you would save by paying the lower price.

Toy	Number Sentence	Amount Saved
cow		
horse		
pig		
sheep		
goat		
duck		

Colour the item that costs less.
Write a number sentence to show how much less the item costs.

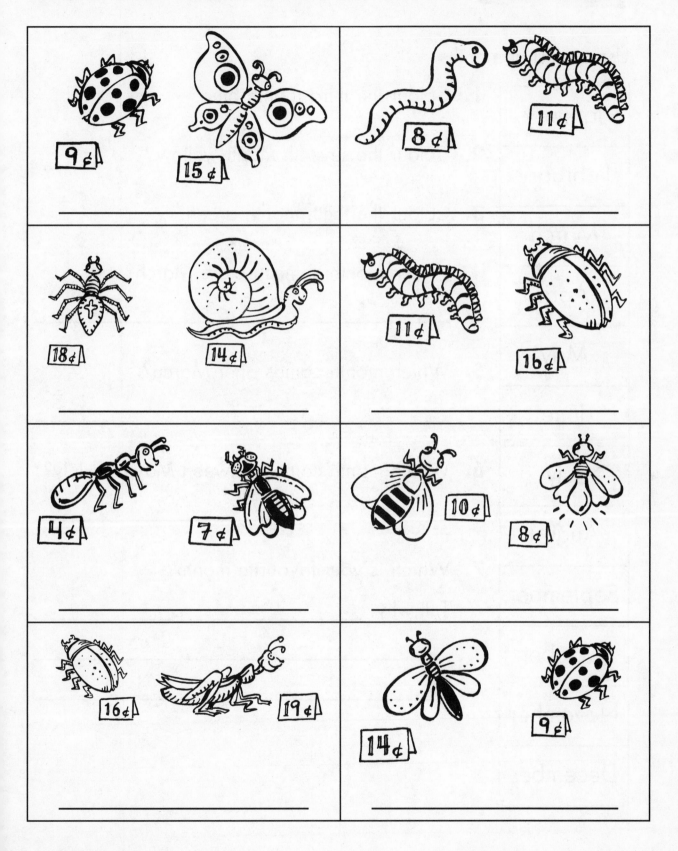

_____

_____

_____

_____

_____

_____

_____

_____

🏠 **FAMILY NOTE:** Your child has been solving problems that involve comparing prices to find the difference. Provide small objects such as buttons or pennies to help your child find the answers.

Naming the Months

Use the list of months.

| January |
| February |
| March |
| April |
| May |
| June |
| July |
| August |
| September |
| October |
| November |
| December |

1. Colour the third month blue.

2. Colour the seventh month yellow.

3. Colour the tenth month green.

4. Which month comes before March?

_____

5. Which month comes after March?

_____

6. Which month comes between May and July?

_____

7. Which is your favourite month?
Tell why. _____

_____

_____

Play this game with a friend or family member.
You will need one number cube and two different markers.

Put your markers on Start.
Take turns.

1. Roll the number cube.

2. Move your marker that number of spaces.

3. If you land on a shaded space, follow the directions.

4. Play until one of you lands on Finish.

A Race Through the Months

Start	January	February	Go ahead to May.	March	April
					Go back to February.
September	August	July	Go back to April.	June	May
Go back to August.					
October	Go ahead to December	November	Go back to July.	December	**Finish**

⌂ **FAMILY NOTE:** This game will give your child practice in reading the names of the months and in putting months in sequence. Play the game several times and keep track of who wins each time. If you do not have a number cube (die), you could write the numbers from 1 to 6 on small papers and draw one from a paper bag on each turn.

UNIT
3
ACTIVITY
2

Estimating Time

Show two things you can do in one minute.
Use pictures, words, and numbers.

Show two things you can do in five minutes.
Use pictures, words, and numbers.

Estimate how many times you can do each activity in one minute.
Ask a family member to time one minute as you try each activity.

Activity	Estimate	Actual Number
jump up and down		
write the number 3		
sing "Happy Birthday"		
tap your foot		
say the alphabet		
draw a happy face		
You choose. _____		

Can you tell how long one minute is?
Tell a helper when to start timing, and when you think one minute
has passed.

FAMILY NOTE: The activities on this page will help your child develop a sense of how long one minute is. Ask your child what she or he can do in five or ten minutes.

Measuring Time

Write each time.

7:00 _____   _____   _____

_____   _____   _____

Draw hands on the clock to show each time.

8:00   6:30   5:00

Write each time.
Tell how long each activity takes.

Camp Activities

Activity	Starting Time	Finishing Time	How Long It Takes
swimming			
crafts			
baseball			
story time			

FAMILY NOTE: Your child is learning to find elapsed time. You can help your child with this concept by asking questions such as, "What time will it be in one hour? in two hours? in five hours?" or "What time was it three hours ago?"

41

Identifying the Shapes on Solids

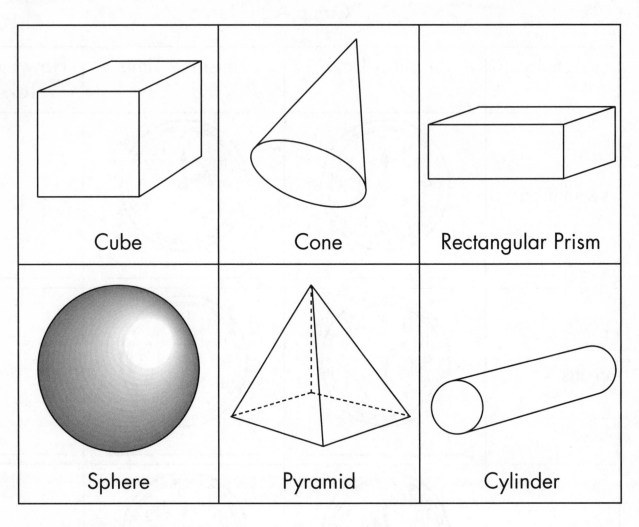

Cube · Cone · Rectangular Prism

Sphere · Pyramid · Cylinder

Write the name of a solid to answer each riddle.
Use Power Solids to help you.

1. I have all ▭ faces. _____

2. I have no faces. _____

3. I have some △ faces. _____

4. I have all ▢ faces. _____

5. I have six faces. _____

6. I am shaped like a ball. _____

7. I am shaped like a juice tin. _____

Play this game with a friend or family member.
You will need a paper clip, a pencil, and 16 pennies.

Take turns.

1. Spin the paper clip around the pencil point to work the spinner. Name the shape.

2. Find a solid on the game board that has the shape you spun. Cover it with a penny.

3. Keep playing until all the solids are covered.

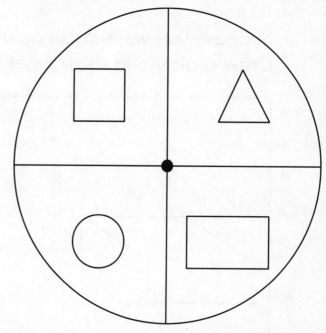

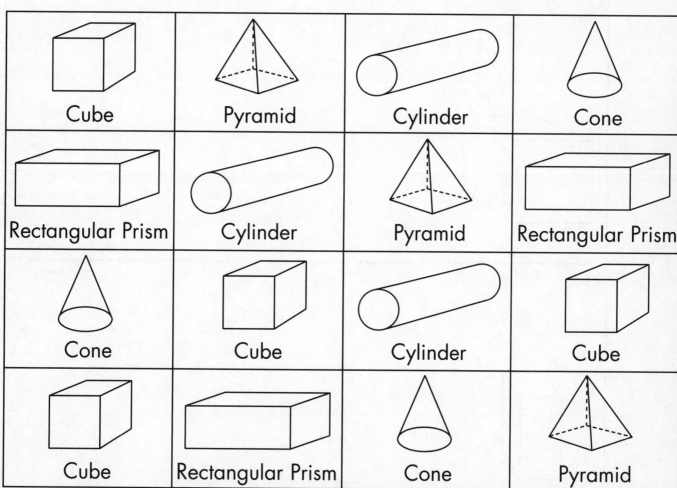

Cube	Pyramid	Cylinder	Cone
Rectangular Prism	Cylinder	Pyramid	Rectangular Prism
Cone	Cube	Cylinder	Cube
Cube	Rectangular Prism	Cone	Pyramid

FAMILY NOTE: Your child has been learning about geometric solids. This game will give your child practice in finding two-dimensional shapes on three-dimensional solids.

43

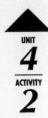

Relating Boxes to Their Patterns

Suppose you were to cut open each box and flatten it.
Draw a picture to show what it would look like.

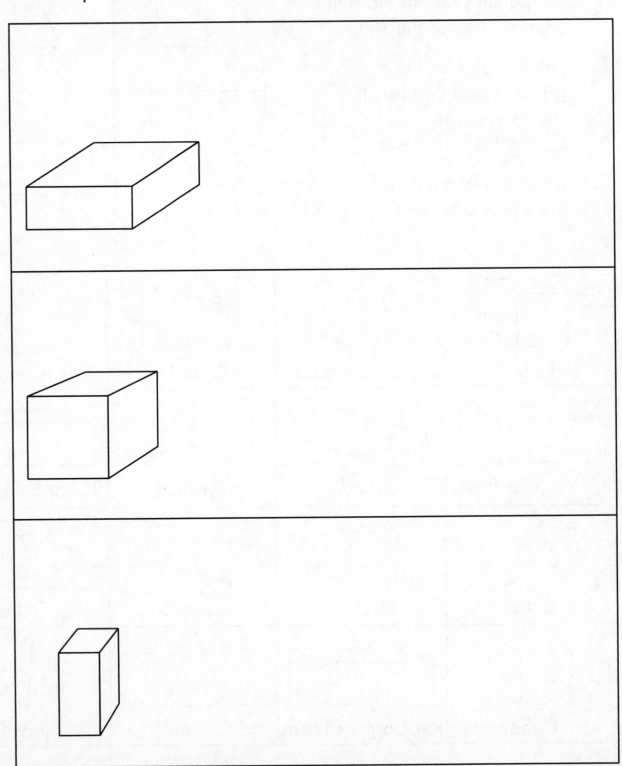

Here is a pattern for a box.
Trace the pattern on paper.
Cut it out.

Add pictures and writing to the pattern.
Make the pattern look like a package for a product.
Then fold and tape your package.

Describe your package.

_____

_____

_____

FAMILY NOTE: Your child has been examining the two-dimensional shapes that form a three-dimensional object. Ask your child to tell you the number and shape of the faces (flat surfaces) on the box.

Covering Shapes

Find two ways to cover the large hexagon with Pattern Blocks.
For each way, record how many blocks of each type you used.

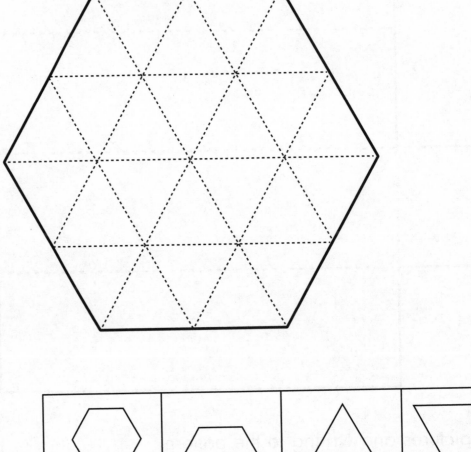

first way				
second way				

Ask a friend to cover the hexagon using the numbers of blocks
you recorded.

Colour these Pattern Block shapes in the design.
Make an interesting pattern.

Yellow   Red   Blue   Green

Write about your pattern.

_____

_____

_____

_____

🏠 **FAMILY NOTE:** Your child has been covering shapes with various arrangements of Pattern Blocks. This helps your child understand that shapes can be composed of other shapes. Ask your child which Pattern Block shape she or he used most and least often in the pattern.

Exploring with Tangrams

Make each triangle with tangram pieces from Activity Master 24.
Draw dotted lines to show where you put the pieces.

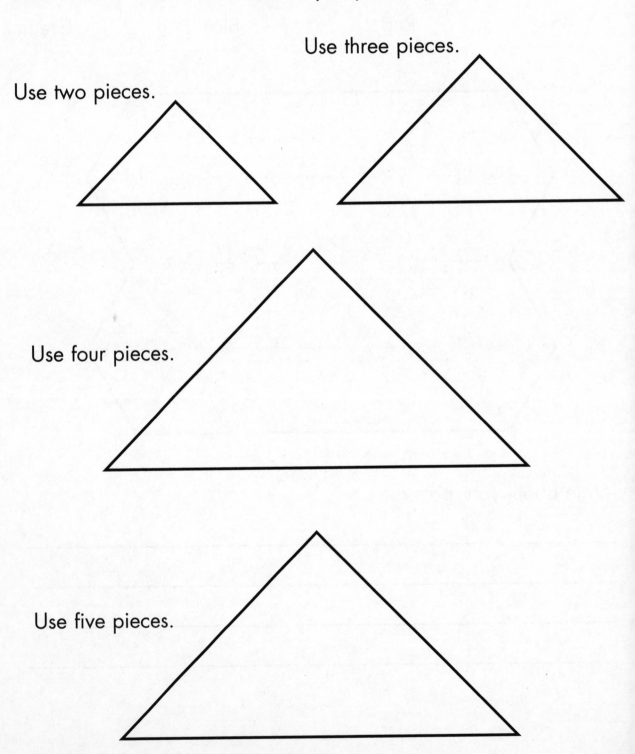

Use three pieces.

Use two pieces.

Use four pieces.

Use five pieces.

Make each rectangle with tangram pieces from Activity Master 24.
Draw dotted lines to show where you put the pieces.

Use three pieces.

Use four pieces.

Use five pieces.

Use six pieces.

FAMILY NOTE: Your child has been using pieces from a seven-piece puzzle called a tangram to investigate how shapes can combine to form other shapes. Ask your child to show you some other shapes that can be made with tangram pieces.

49

Making Patterns that Grow

Fill each ◇ with tan Pattern Blocks.
Record how many you used.

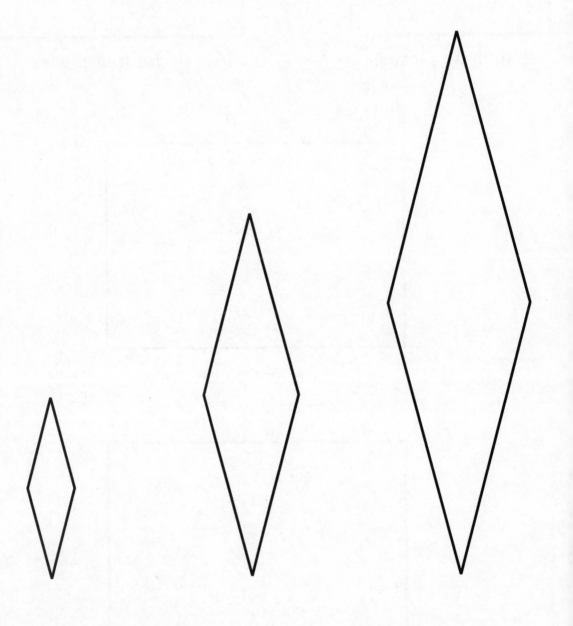

_____   _____   _____

Build the next ◇ in the pattern.
Tell how many tan Pattern Blocks you used. _____

Draw the next shape in each growing pattern.

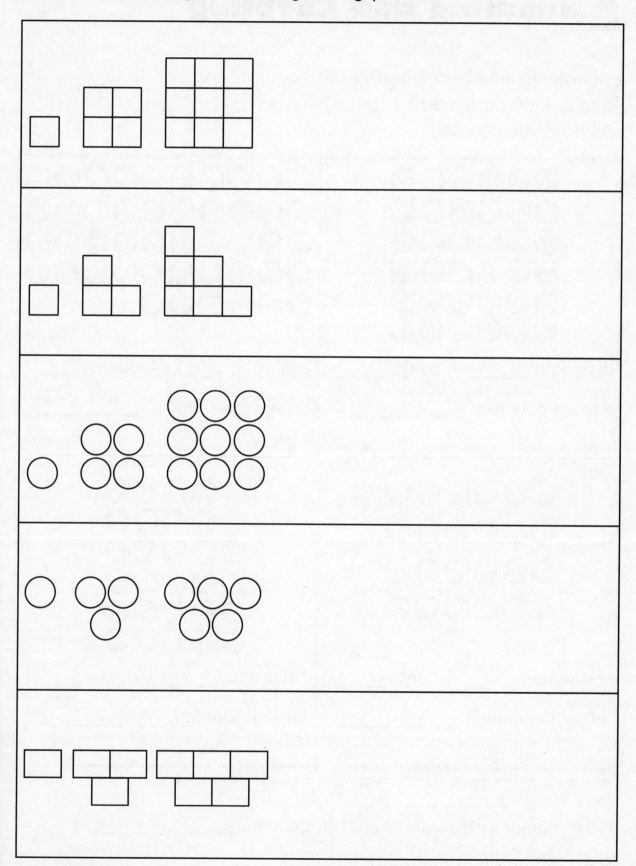

FAMILY NOTE: Your child has been exploring patterns that grow. Ask your child to describe each growth pattern and to tell how she or he determined what the next diagram would look like.

51

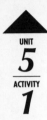

Estimating and Counting

Estimate the number of marbles in each group.
Then decide on a way to count them.
Tell how you counted.

Estimate: _____ Count: _____

How I counted: _____

_____

Estimate: _____ Count: _____

How I counted: _____

_____

Estimate: _____ Count: _____

How I counted: _____

_____

Estimate: _____ Count: _____

How I counted: _____

_____

How many marbles are there altogether? _____

How did you find the total? _____

_____

You will need two containers of small objects such as beans or buttons.
Take three handfuls from one container.
Estimate the number of objects you took.
Then count.
Draw and write to show how you counted.

Repeat with three handfuls from the other container.

Container 1	Container 2
Estimate: _____	Estimate: _____
Count: _____	Count: _____
How I counted: _____	How I counted: _____
_____	_____

How many objects did you take altogether? _____

How did you find the total? _____

_____

🏠 **FAMILY NOTE:** Your child has been estimating and counting collections of objects, and then combining the collections to find the total number. Encourage your child to count the objects by 2s, 3s, 5s, or 10s.

UNIT
5
ACTIVITY
2

Counting Large Quantities

Take five handfuls of each item.
Estimate how many of each item you took.
Then count.
Tell how you counted.

Item	My Estimate	My Count	How I Counted
Link-Its			
Snap Cubes			
buttons			
counters			
You choose.			

54

Estimate how many small objects it will take to fill this rectangle.
Fill the rectangle. Do not pile the objects.
Then count.

Tell how you counted.

Objects I used: _____

My estimate: _____   My count: _____

How I counted: _____

_____

🏠 **FAMILY NOTE:** Please provide small objects, such as dried beans, toothpicks, or popcorn kernels, for this activity. Ask your child to explain how she or he kept track of the count.

UNIT
5
ACTIVITY
3

Grouping to Count

Estimate the number of leaves.
Circle equal groups. Then count.

My estimate: _____

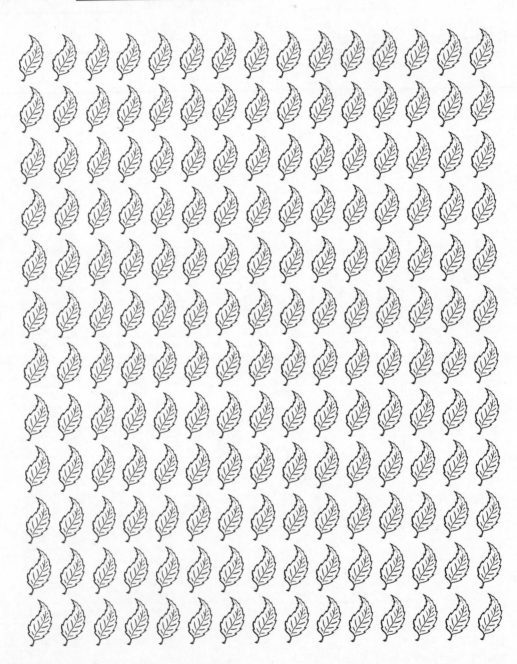

My count: _____

How I counted: _____

Estimate how many small objects will fit in a container.

Fill the container.
Then put the objects in groups and count.

What did you fill the container with?

_____

How many did you estimate? _____

How many did you count? _____

Draw a picture to show how you grouped to count.

⌂ **FAMILY NOTE:** Your child has been learning that arranging objects in groups makes it easier to count. Please provide a container, such as a margarine tub, and a collection of small objects, such as dried beans, popcorn kernels, or pennies. Encourage your child to organize the objects in groups of 2, 3, 5, or 10 and to skip-count to find the total.

57

UNIT
5
ACTIVITY
4

Comparing Quantities

Work with a partner.
Each person takes a handful of items.
Group your items for counting.
Record your work in the chart.

Item	How I Grouped	My Count	My Partner's Count	Who Has More?
buttons				
beans				
Snap Cubes				
Link-Its				
You choose.				

58

Take a handful of small objects.
Group the objects.
Colour squares to show your groups.
Ask a family member to do the same.

How I Grouped   How My Family Member
                                         Grouped

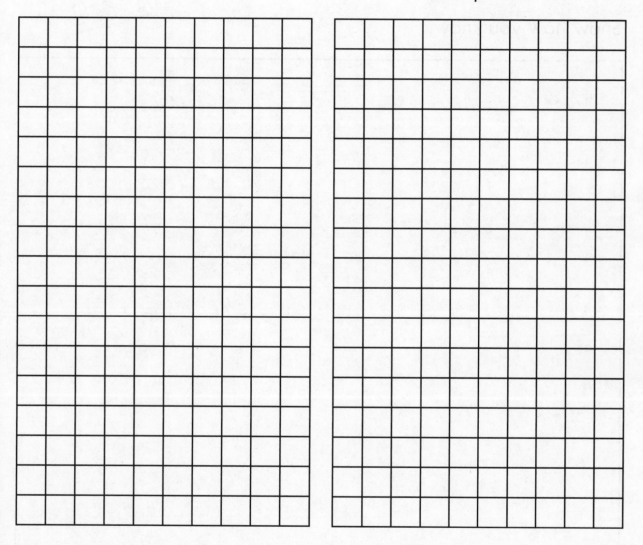

Which objects did you use? _____

Who has more? _____

🏠 **FAMILY NOTE:** Your child is learning to compare large quantities of objects. Provide small objects, such as toothpicks, buttons, or dried beans, for this
activity. Ask your child to compare the two sets of objects visually and then to skip-count to verify.

59

Grouping by Tens

You want to buy 150 seeds.
How many packages of 10 seeds
will you buy?

Show how you know.

I will buy _____ packages of 10 seeds.

60

Circle groups of 10 seeds.
How many tens are in each number?

130 seeds	90 seeds
_____ tens in 130	_____ tens in 90
160 seeds	140 seeds
_____ tens in 160	_____ tens in 140

⌂ **FAMILY NOTE:** Your child has been using various methods to count tens in different numbers. Grouping by tens helps your child develop an understanding of place value.

UNIT
5
ACTIVITY
6

Composing Numbers

Here is one way to build 243:

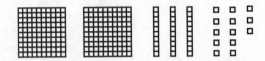

243 = 2 hundreds + 3 tens + 13 ones

Use blocks from Activity Masters 25 and 26.
Build 243 two other ways.
Use pictures and numbers to show each way.

243 = _____ hundreds + _____ tens + _____ ones

243 = _____ hundreds + _____ tens + _____ ones

To the Teacher: Please provide copies of Activity Masters 25 and 26 for modelling numbers on this page and on page 63.

Use blocks from Activity Masters 25 and 26.
Show how to build each number using as few blocks as possible.
Use pictures and numbers to show what you did.

263	175
_2_ hundreds _6_ tens _3_ ones	___ hundreds ___ tens ___ ones
96	**387**
___ hundreds ___ tens ___ ones	___ hundreds ___ tens ___ ones
428	**104**
___ hundreds ___ tens ___ ones	___ hundreds ___ tens ___ ones

🏠 **FAMILY NOTE:** Your child has been using place value models to make two- and three-digit numbers. Ask your child to use the hundreds, tens, and ones models on Activity Masters 25 and 26 to build each number.

Comparing and Ordering Numbers

Write the scores.
Circle the greater score in each pair.

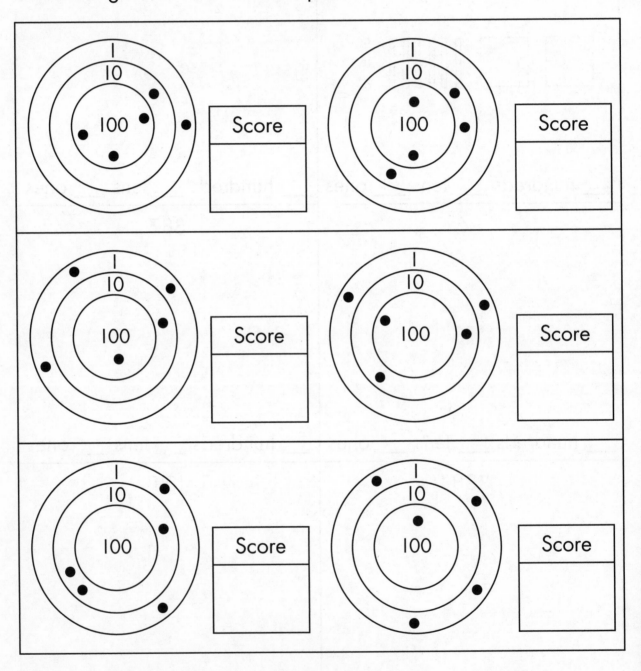

Write the circled numbers in order from least to greatest.

Play this game with a friend or family member.
Spin a paper clip around a pencil to work the spinner.

Here's how to play:

1. Each player spins the spinner three times and records the results in order as a three-digit number.

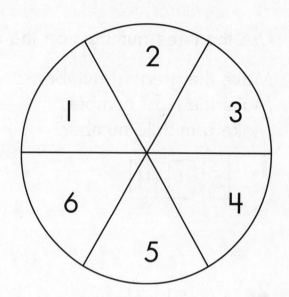

2. Compare the three-digit numbers in each round.

3. Circle the greater number.

4. Play five rounds.

	Player 1	Player 2
Round 1		
Round 2		
Round 3		
Round 4		
Round 5		

Write the circled numbers in order from least to greatest.

_____

_____

🏠 **FAMILY NOTE:** Your child is learning to compare and order three-digit numbers. Ask your child to explain his or her strategies for determining the greater number in each pair and for putting the five numbers in order.

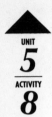

Ordering Numbers

Use the three numbers on the cards.

Make the greatest number.
Make the least number.
Make a middle number.

1. | 5 | 1 | 4 |

Greatest number: _____

Least number: _____

Middle number: _____

2. | 3 | 2 | 7 |

Greatest number: _____

Least number:_____

Middle number: _____

3. | 4 | 8 | 6 |

Greatest number: _____

Least number: _____

Middle number: _____

4. | 2 | 3 | 4 |

Greatest number: _____

Least number: _____

Middle number: _____

5. | 6 | 3 | 5 |

Greatest number: _____

Least number: _____

Middle number: _____

Write each set of numbers in order from least to greatest.

1. 245 127 631 _____ _____ _____

2. 584 273 425 _____ _____ _____

3. 580 721 595 _____ _____ _____

4. 635 583 631 _____ _____ _____

5. 786 743 727 _____ _____ _____

6. 125 432 381 _____ _____ _____

7. 317 524 262 _____ _____ _____

8. 222 163 512 _____ _____ _____

FAMILY NOTE: The work on this page will help to consolidate your child's understanding of place value. As your child compares the numbers in each set, help him or her focus on how many hundreds, tens, and ones are in each number. Ask why it helps to compare the hundreds digits first.

Skip-Counting

Show two counting patterns on the chart.
Colour squares to show one pattern.
Circle numbers to show the other pattern.

101	102	103	104	105	106	107	108	109	110
111	112	113	114	115	116	117	118	119	120
121	122	123	124	125	126	127	128	129	130
131	132	133	134	135	136	137	138	139	140
141	142	143	144	145	146	147	148	149	150
151	152	153	154	155	156	157	158	159	160
161	162	163	164	165	166	167	168	169	170
171	172	173	174	175	176	177	178	179	180
181	182	183	184	185	186	187	188	189	190
191	192	193	194	195	196	197	198	199	200

Write about your patterns.

_____

_____

_____

_____

Continue each counting pattern.
Use the chart on page 68 to help you.

100, 110, 120, ____, ____, ____, ____, ____

95, 100, 105, ____, ____, ____, ____, ____, ____, ____, ____

140, 142, 144, ____, ____, ____, ____, ____

145, 150, 155, ____, ____, ____, ____, ____

115, 125, 135, ____, ____, ____, ____, ____

184, 186, 188, ____, ____, ____, ____, ____

128, 138, 148, ____, ____, ____, ____, ____

🏠 **FAMILY NOTE:** Your child has been exploring skip-counting patterns beyond 100. You may want to have your child use a calculator to verify each skip-counting pattern. If the calculator has a constant feature, you can continue an addition counting pattern by entering the pattern and pressing ⌷=⌷ repeatedly. For example, to count from 100 by 10s, enter ⌷100⌷ ⌷+⌷ ⌷10⌷ ⌷=⌷ ⌷=⌷ ⌷=⌷ ....

Adding Large Numbers

Solve each problem any way you choose. Show your work.

1. Mr. Tanaka and Mrs. Everett are taking their classes to the zoo. How many children are going to the zoo?

Classes at Oak Street School	
Teacher	Number of Students
Ms. Beale	24
Mr. Tanaka	28
Mr. Zane	29
Mrs. Everett	27
Miss Sung	28
Ms. Green	31
Mr. Santos	32

2. Ms. Beale's and Mr. Zane's classes are getting together to watch a video. How many children will there be?

3. Ms. Green and Miss Sung are taking their classes to see a play. How many children are going to the play?

4. Make up your own problem about two classes at Oak Street School. Show how you would solve your problem.

Solve each problem any way you choose.
Show how you solved it.

---

25 children in Grade 1
14 children in Grade 2
How many children in all? _____

---

29 children playing ball
14 children skipping
How many children in all? _____

---

30 children in the water
17 children on the sand
How many children in all? _____

---

36 children wearing hats
35 children not wearing hats
How many children in all? _____

---

13 children standing
28 children sitting
How many children in all? _____

FAMILY NOTE: Your child is learning to use her or his own strategies to solve problems that involve adding two-digit numbers. Ask your child to explain how he or she solved the problems on this page.

UNIT
6
ACTIVITY
2

Finding Combinations and Costs

1. Suppose you want to buy one snack and one drink.
Draw pictures to show all the possible combinations.
The first one is done for you.

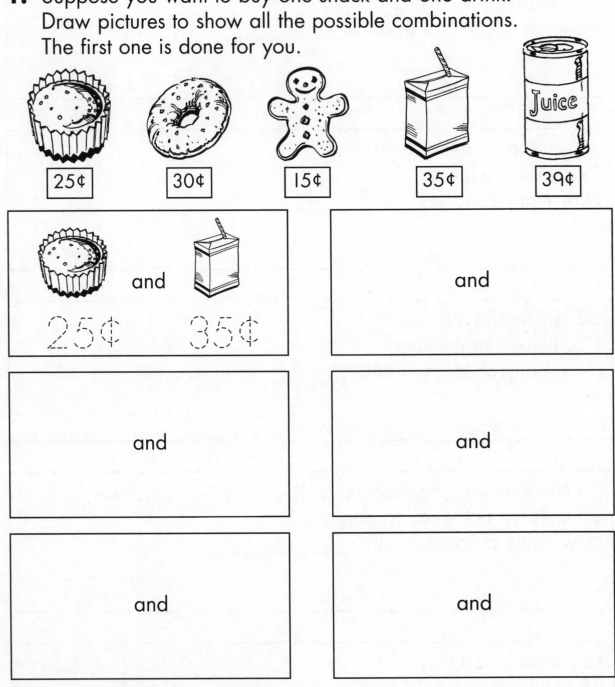

2. Choose one combination.
Find the total cost. Show all your work.

Work with a friend or family member. Take turns.
Circle two items to buy.
Record the prices on the chart.

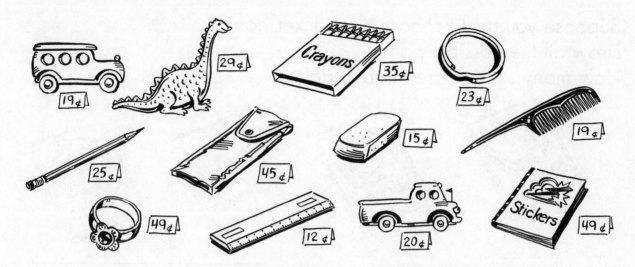

Use any method you wish. Find the total cost of each pair.
Show all your work.
Keep playing until all the items are gone.

My Work	My Partner's Work

Finding Totals

Suppose you could choose two sticker books.
Draw all the possible pairs.
How many stickers are in each pair?

Sticker Book Pairs	How Many Stickers in the Pair?
and	
and	
and	
and	
and	
and	

Play this game with a family member.
Take turns.
You will need a pencil and a paper clip to work the spinner.

1. Spin the spinner twice.
Add the two numbers.
Record your work.

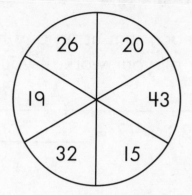

2. Take five turns each.
If you spin a pair you
already added, spin again.

My Work	My Partner's Work

🏠 **FAMILY NOTE:** Your child is continuing to develop her or his own methods of adding two-digit numbers. Ask your child to explain the methods she or he used. Share your methods with your child.

Using Strategies to Add Large Numbers

Find each sum using any method you wish.
Show all your work. If you need help, turn to page 165.

1. 33 + 47 = _____

2. 27 + 15 = _____

3. 72 + 13 = _____

4. 41 + 30 = _____

5. 16 + 18 = _____

6. 21 + 29 = _____

Find each sum using any method you wish.
Show all your work.

Ask a family member to do Problems 1 and 4 on paper.
Explain your methods to each other.

1. 24 + 33 = _____	**2.** 19 + 19 = _____
3. 52 + 14 = _____	**4.** 35 + 46 = _____
5. 49 + 18 = _____	**6.** 36 + 25 = _____

⌂ **FAMILY NOTE:** To find the sums, your child may wish to use the standard procedure or a personal method that makes sense to him or her. Share your procedures for adding with your child and have your child compare his or her procedures with yours. Refer to page 165 to see several strategies that can be used to add.

UNIT
6
ACTIVITY
5

Estimating to Reach a Target Sum

Choose a number to add so each sum will reach the target.
Use a calculator to help you.

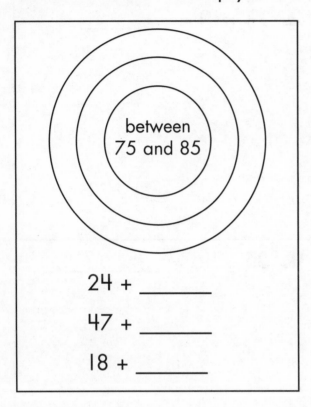

between
75 and 85

24 + _____

47 + _____

18 + _____

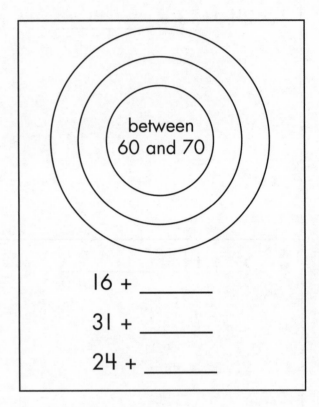

between
60 and 70

16 + _____

31 + _____

24 + _____

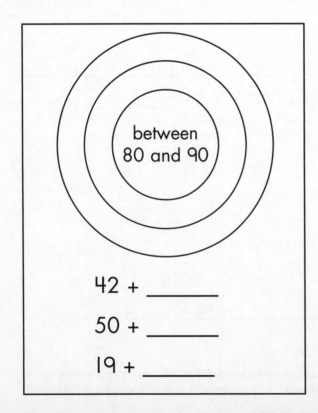

between
80 and 90

42 + _____

50 + _____

19 + _____

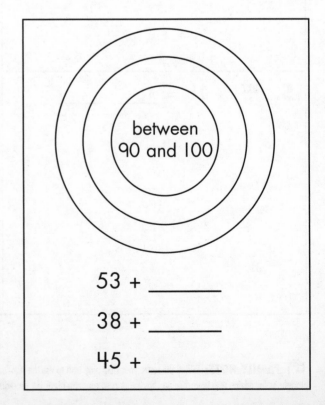

between
90 and 100

53 + _____

38 + _____

45 + _____

Play this estimation game with a family member.
You will need a calculator.

Getting Close to 100

1. Take turns. Choose two numbers from the box that you estimate will give a sum close to 100.

2. Use the calculator to find each sum.
Record each sum in the chart.

3. Decide whose sum is closer to 100. Circle it.

4. Play five more rounds.
You can use a number more than once if you like.

5. Talk about the estimation strategies you used.

29	31	35	45
82	22	25	27
	36		53
15		74	70
	46		
85		80	73
	63		
72	20	50	64

Player 1	Player 2

FAMILY NOTE: Your child is learning to estimate the answers to addition problems. Encourage your child to explain how he or she chose the numbers in this game. Explain your methods to your child.

Using Subtraction to Compare

Compare the two groups in each graph.
Write a subtraction sentence to find the difference.

Do You Have a Pet?

yes

no

_____

How Old Are You?

7

8

_____

Do You Like Spinach?

yes ☺☺☺☺☺☺☺☺☺☺☺

no ☹☹☹☹☹☹☹☹☹☹☹☹☹

_____

Which Game Do You Like Best?

hopscotch	Marina	J.D.	Bill	Jan	Denis	Maria	Alex	Liu	Audrey	Joelle	David
dodgeball	Trisha	Kenji	Anita	Paula	Jaime	Jill	Nancy	Keith	Ali		

_____

Work with a family member.

You will need some small objects such as pennies, buttons, or dried beans.

Each person takes a handful of objects.
Players count their objects and record the numbers in the chart.

Subtract to find how many more objects one person has than the other.

Number of Objects for Player 1	Number of Objects for Player 2	Subtraction Sentence

UNIT
6
ACTIVITY
7

Subtracting to Find the Change

Colour one item you would like to buy.
How much change will you get?

Show your work.

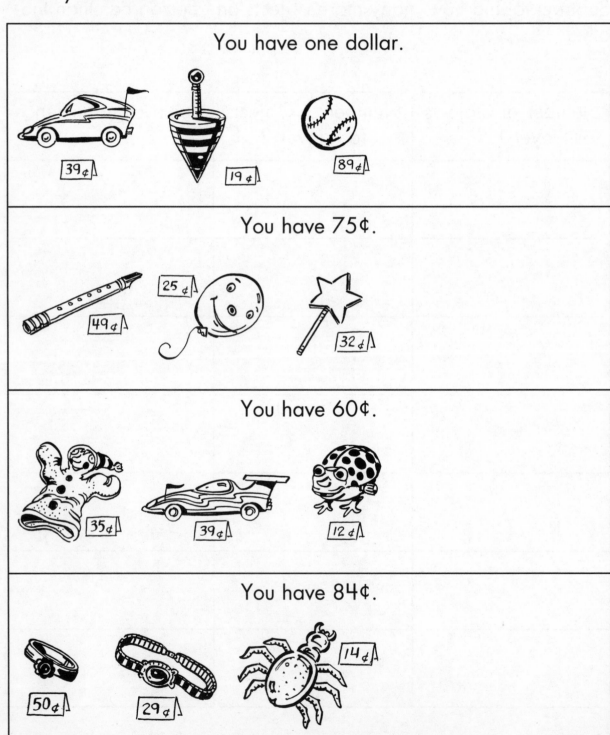

You have one dollar.

39¢   19¢   89¢

You have 75¢.

49¢   25¢   32¢

You have 60¢.

35¢   39¢   12¢

You have 84¢.

50¢   29¢   14¢

82

Play this game with a family member.
You will need a pencil and a paper clip to work the spinner.

1. Spin the spinner to see how much money you have to spend.

2. Choose an item to buy.

3. Figure out how much change you will get.

4. Record your work in the chart. Ask your partner to make a recording chart on a sheet of paper.

5. Take turns until all the items are gone.

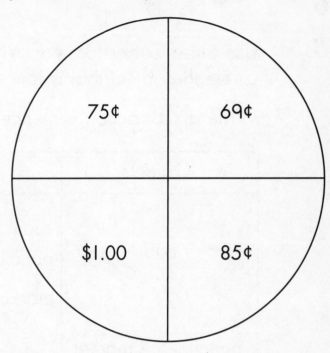

How Much I Have to Spend	Price of What I Bought	My Change

🏠 **FAMILY NOTE:** Your child is learning to figure out how much change will be left after a purchase. There are many different ways to calculate the change. Ask your child to explain the methods she or he used. Share your methods with your child.

Comparing Measurements

Use Snap Cubes to measure each pair of objects.
Circle the object that is longer.

Write a subtraction sentence to show the difference.

Objects	Measures	Subtraction Sentence
and pencil marker	pencil: _____ cubes marker: _____ cubes	
and table bulletin board	table: _____ cubes bulletin board: _____ cubes	
and table leg chair leg	table leg: ___ cubes chair leg: ___ cubes	
and math book box	math book: __ cubes box: _____ cubes	

84

Find and measure each pair of objects.
Record the measures and the units you used.
Circle the object that is longer.

Write a number sentence to show the difference.

Objects	Measures	Difference
and spoon fork	spoon: _____ _____ fork: _____ _____	
and magazine book	magazine: _____ _____ book: _____ _____	
and my shoe someone else's shoe	my shoe: _____ _____ someone else's shoe: _____ _____	
You choose. and	_____ : _____ _____ : _____	

FAMILY NOTE: Your child is learning that subtraction can be used to find the difference between the lengths of two objects. Please provide some small, uniform objects such as pennies, dried beans, or paper clips for your child to use as units of measure.

Using Strategies to Subtract Large Numbers

Find each difference using any method you wish.
Show all your work. If you need help, turn to page 169 in this book.

1. 36 – 22 = _____	**2.** 78 – 53 = _____
3. 62 – 47 = _____	**4.** 51 – 20 = _____
5. 40 – 18 = _____	**6.** 27 – 15 = _____

Find each difference using any method you wish.
Show all your work.

Ask a family member to do Problems 2 and 4 on paper.
Explain your methods to one another.

1. 85 – 31 = _____	**2.** 68 – 33 = _____
3. 94 – 50 = _____	**4.** 41 – 25 = _____
5. 73 – 58 = _____	**6.** 30 – 14 = _____

Using Coins to Show One Dollar

Draw more coins so each set equals one dollar.

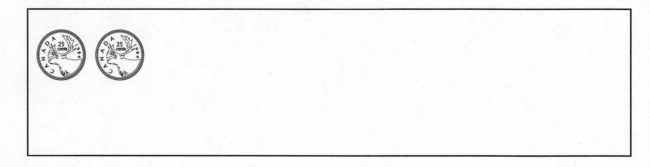

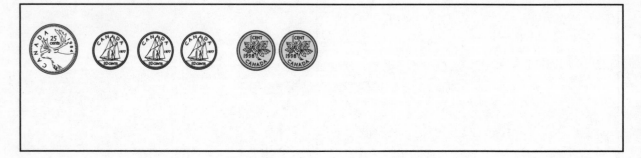

Draw coins to make one dollar. Use more than five coins.

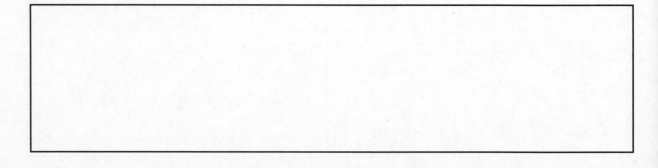

To the Teacher: You may wish to send home copies of Activity Master 32 so students can make paper coins for the game described on page 89.

Play this game with a friend or family member.

You will need: 6 small pieces of cardboard numbered 1 to 6
2 different buttons to use as markers
a collection of quarters, dimes, nickels, and
pennies (or paper copies from Activity Master 32)
a paper bag

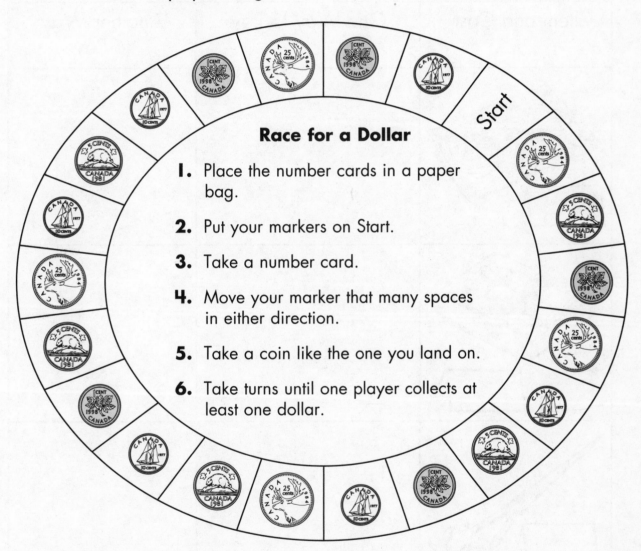

Race for a Dollar

Start

1. Place the number cards in a paper bag.

2. Put your markers on Start.

3. Take a number card.

4. Move your marker that many spaces in either direction.

5. Take a coin like the one you land on.

6. Take turns until one player collects at least one dollar.

Write what you learned as you played this game.

_____

_____

_____

🏠 **FAMILY NOTE:** Your child is learning to count money and to make a collection of coins equal to one dollar. Play the game several times. As you play, encourage your child to make coin trades. For example, when your child accumulates two dimes and a nickel, suggest that these could be traded for a quarter.

UNIT
7
ACTIVITY
2

Using Coins to Buy

Write an amount less than one dollar on each price tag.
Draw two different coin sets you could use to pay for each item.

Item and Cost	One Way to Pay	Another Way to Pay

Find four food packages at home that you think each cost less than one dollar.
Draw a picture of each package.
Write a price for each one.

Draw coins to show how to pay for each package.
Use as few coins as possible.

FAMILY NOTE: Your child is learning how to use coins to pay for items that cost less than one dollar. Please provide some pennies, nickels, dimes, and quarters so your child can explore ways to pay for each item.

91

Measuring Many Attributes

Choose objects to measure.
Choose measuring tools.

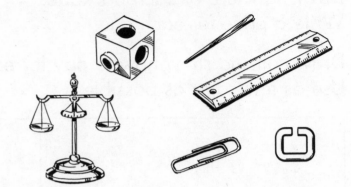

Draw pictures.
Record the measurements.

What to Measure	Object	Measuring Tool	Measurement
How long?			
How tall?			
How wide?			
How heavy?			

Choose objects at home to measure.

Measure each object.
Use a part of your body as a measuring tool.

What to Measure	Measuring Tool	Object	Measurement
How tall?	your hand		
How long?	your foot		
How wide?	your finger		
You choose.	You choose.		

⌂ **FAMILY NOTE:** Your child is learning to identify attributes of size such as height, width, and length, and to measure these attributes using nonstandard units such as paper clips, straws, and body parts. Before your child measures, encourage him or her to estimate.

Measuring Distance

Measure each distance.

From	To	Measuring Tool	Measurement
the floor	the top of the doorknob	straws	
the seat of your chair	the floor	Snap Cubes	
your belly button	the floor	Link-Its	
one end of your desk	the other end of your desk	toothpicks	

Why is it hard to tell which is the greatest distance?

_____

_____

_____

_____

Hold a Mini-Olympics with two friends or family members.
You will need straws or toothpicks to use as measuring tools.

Try each event three times.
Measure each distance.
Record your best result for each event in the chart.

Cottonball Toss

Toss a cottonball
or a crumpled-up
tissue as far as you can.
Measure the distance.

Javelin Throw

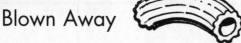

Throw a cotton
swab or a toothpick
as far as you can.
Measure the distance.

Blown Away

Place a piece of uncooked macaroni or a dried
bean on the table. Blow it as far as you
can in one breath. Measure the distance.

Name	Cottonball Toss	Javelin Throw	Blown Away

FAMILY NOTE: Your child is learning to use nonstandard units to measure distance. When your child records the distances for each event, remind her or him to record both the number and the unit, for example, 12 toothpicks.

Comparing Measurements

Use Snap Cubes.

Measure your distance.
Then measure your friend's distance.
Circle the greater distance.

What to Measure	My Distance	My Friend's Distance
from your shoulder to the floor	_____ cubes	_____ cubes
from your knee to your waist	_____ cubes	_____ cubes
a giant step	_____ cubes	_____ cubes
two baby steps	_____ cubes	_____ cubes

Use straws or toothpicks.

Measure your distance.
Record the measures and the units you used.
Then measure a family member's distance.
Circle the greater distance.

What to Measure	My Distance	My Partner's Distance
How far can you blow a penny across a smooth surface in one breath?		
How far can you roll a penny on its edge?		
How far can you flick a penny with your finger?		
How far can you hop with a penny balanced on your foot?		

FAMILY NOTE: Your child is learning that measurements are easier to compare when they are expressed with common units. Please provide either straws or toothpicks for measuring distances. Encourage your child to record partial units in some way. For example, your child might write "about 12 toothpicks" or "a little more than 12 toothpicks."

97

Modelling Measurements

Here is a fairy tale giant.
Look at his measurements.

Work with a partner.
Use a metre stick.
Cut a piece of string
to show the length of
the giant's foot.

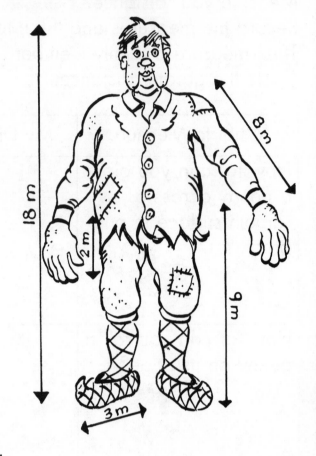

Estimate how many of your
feet it would take to equal
the length of the giant's foot.
Then measure.

My estimate: _____ of my feet

My measurement: ____ of my feet

Repeat the activity for two other measurements.
Record your work in the chart.

Giant's Body Part	My Estimate	Measurement
hand	____ of my hands	____ of my hands
You choose.		

98

Ask a family member to help you cut a piece of string or wool to match each measure shown in the chart.

Measure each string with the measuring tool shown in the chart. Record your estimates and measurements.

Item	Measuring Tool	Estimate	Measurement
bus	giant steps		
tree	foot		
garage door	hand span		

Measuring in Centimetres

Use a ruler or tape measure.
Measure each pair of lengths to the nearest centimetre.
Colour the object in each pair that is longer, wider, or taller.

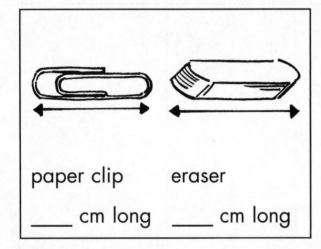

paper clip   eraser

____ cm long   ____ cm long

math book   story book

____ cm wide   ____ cm wide

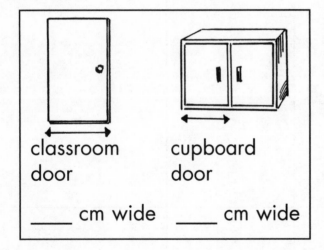

classroom   cupboard
door   door

____ cm wide   ____ cm wide

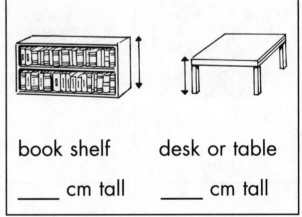

book shelf   desk or table

____ cm tall   ____ cm tall

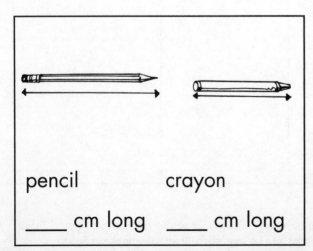

pencil   crayon

____ cm long   ____ cm long

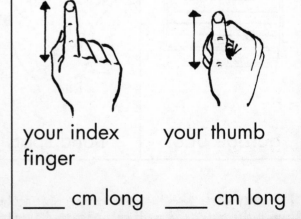

your index   your thumb
finger

____ cm long   ____ cm long

Find objects to measure.
Use a ruler or a tape measure.
Measure to the nearest centimetre.

What to Measure	Object	Measure
something longer than your arm		
something shorter than your foot		
something about as tall as you are		
something wider than a door		

Explain how to measure an object with a ruler or tape measure.

_____

_____

🏠 **FAMILY NOTE:** Your child is learning to measure lengths in centimetres. Help your child align the ruler or tape measure with the object to be measured so the edge is at 0 cm, then read and record the measurement together. Remind your child to record the unit (cm) as well as the number.

Understanding How a Balance Works

Look at each balance.
Answer the questions.

There are 6 cubes in the first cup.
How many cubes might be in the other cup? _____

There are 3 cubes in the first cup.
How many cubes might be in the other cup? _____

There are 5 cubes in the first cup.
How many cubes might be in the other cup? _____

There are 0 cubes in the first cup.
How many cubes might be in the other cup? _____

There are 0 cubes in the first cup.
How many cubes might be in the other cup? _____

There are 8 cubes in the first cup.
How many cubes might be in the other cup? _____

To the Teacher: You may wish to provide students with some of the materials needed for the homework activity on page 103.

Make this string balance with a family member.

You will need: an empty paper towel roll or a ruler you don't
      need any more
      a string 60 cm long
      two paper cups
      glue
      masking tape

1. Tie the piece of string around
the paper towel roll or ruler.

2. Tape the string in place so
it won't slide.

3. Glue or tape the base of a
paper cup to each end.

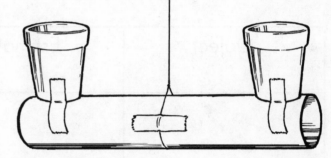

4. Test your balance by putting some small items in the cups.

Explain how your balance works.

_____

_____

_____

_____

_____

_____

FAMILY NOTE: At school, your child learned how to use a hanger to make another type of simple balance. Ask how that balance is similar to or different from the one described on this page. Please save your child's balance. It will be used on the page 105.

Using a Balance

Use the balance you made with a hanger, some paper clips, and two paper cups.

Put an object in one cup.
Estimate how many Link-Its it will take to balance the object.
Put Link-Its into the other cup, one at a time, until the cups balance.
Record your work.

Object	Estimate	How Many Link-Its it Took
crayon		
eraser		
pencil		
chalk		

Write the names of the objects in order from lightest to heaviest.

_____ _____ _____ _____

Estimate which object is heavier.
Then use a balance to check.

Objects	Estimate	Which is Heavier?
penny quarter		
nickel dime		
toothbrush comb		
bottle toothpaste cap lid		
You choose.		

How can you tell which object is heavier?

_____

_____

_____

🏠 **FAMILY NOTE:** Your child is learning to use a balance to compare the masses of objects. Ask your child to find two objects that have about the same mass.

Making Equal Shares

Give each person an equal share.
Draw lines to show where to cut.

2 people

3 people

4 people

4 people

2 people

3 people

3 people

4 people

2 people

Draw lines to divide each shape into equal parts.
Show two different ways.

Number of Equal Parts	First Way	Second Way
2		
3		
4		

FAMILY NOTE: Your child is learning how to divide a whole into equal parts. This helps build an understanding of fractions. Show your child how to use the fraction names "halves," "thirds," and "fourths" as he or she completes this page.

UNIT
9
ACTIVITY
2

Relating Parts to Wholes

Solve each problem.
Show all your work.
Use pictures, numbers, and words.

There are 20 children. Each one gets one-half of a cracker. How many crackers do we need?	
There are 24 children. Each one gets one-third of a fruit bar. How many fruit bars do we need?	
There are 28 children. Each one gets one-fourth of a giant pancake. How many giant pancakes do we need?	

Suppose you are planning a picnic.
There will be 12 children.
How much of each food will you need?

Show all your work.
Use pictures, numbers, and words.

What Each Child Gets	How Many We Need
one-half of a submarine sandwich	
one-third of a bag of chips	
one-fourth of a melon	
one drink	

FAMILY NOTE: Your child is learning to solve problems about fractions of a whole. This page will help your child understand how parts and wholes are related.

Sharing Sets Equally

Share the cookies equally.
Use counters to help you.

Complete the chart.

Number of Cookies	Number of People Sharing	Number of Cookies for Each Person	Fraction of Cookies for Each Person
16	2		
24	4		
15	3		
12	4		
18	3		
22	2		
21	3		

Play this game with a family member.
You will need 24 pennies or other small objects.
Spin a paper clip around a pencil point to work the spinners.

1. Spin the first spinner. Take that many pennies.

2. Spin the second spinner. Put your pennies into that many
equal groups.

3. If you can do this with none left over, you get one point.

4. Take turns until one player has ten points.

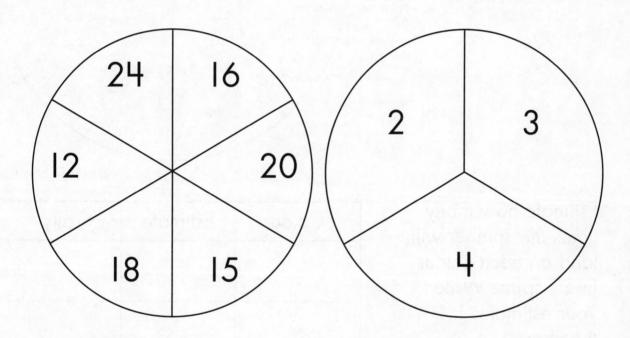

Number of Pennies   Number of Equal Groups

Write what you learned from playing this game.

_____

_____

_____

🏠 **FAMILY NOTE:** Your child is learning how to divide groups of objects into equal sets. This activity will help your child see that some numbers can be divided equally and others cannot.

111

Exploring Spinners

Make a four-colour spinner.
Each colour should have
a fair chance of winning.

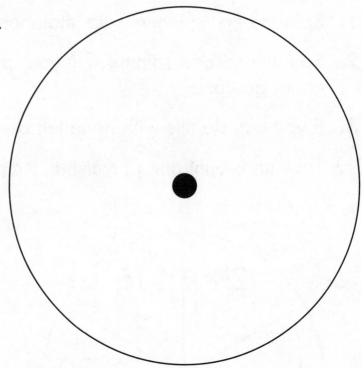

Estimate how many
times the spinner will
land on each colour
in 20 spins. Write
your estimates in
the chart.

Spin 20 times.
Tally the colours
you spin.

Colour	Estimate	Tally

Write what happened.

_____

_____

_____

Make a two-colour spinner.
One colour should be more likely to win than the other colour.

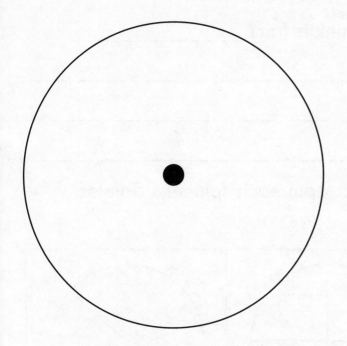

Which colour do you think
is more likely to win?

_____

Estimate how many
times the spinner will
land on each colour
in 20 spins.

Spin 20 times.
Tally the colours
you spin.

Colour	Estimate	Tally

Write what happened.

_____

_____

_____

FAMILY NOTE: Your child has been exploring spinners that are divided into two or more equal or unequal parts. Activities such as this will help your child develop an intuitive understanding of probability.

Exploring Fairness

Which spinner below do you think is fair? _____

Tell why you think so. _____

_____

_____

Use a pencil and a paper clip to spin each spinner 20 times.
Tally the numbers you spin.

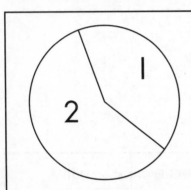
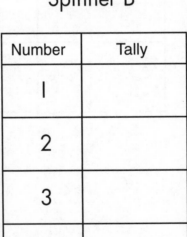

Spinner A

Number	Tally
1	
2	

Spinner B

Number	Tally
1	
2	
3	
4	

Spinner C

Number	Tally
1	
2	
3	

Write what happened. _____

_____

Make each spinner.
Estimate how many times the spinner will land on each colour in 30 spins.

Spin 30 times.
Tally the colours you spin.
Write to tell what happened.

1. Make a three-colour spinner that is fair.

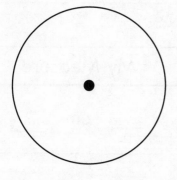

Colour	Estimate	Tally

What happened? _____

_____

_____

2. Make a three-colour spinner that is not fair.

Colour	Estimate	Tally

What happened? _____

_____

_____

FAMILY NOTE: Your child is learning that spinners divided into equal parts are fair, and that spinners divided into unequal parts are unfair. Work with both kinds of spinners helps your child understand how the design of a spinner can affect the outcome.

Measuring Many Attributes

Zena traced a leaf on grid paper.

Use Zena's leaf to complete the chart.
Estimate first, then measure with a ruler and string.

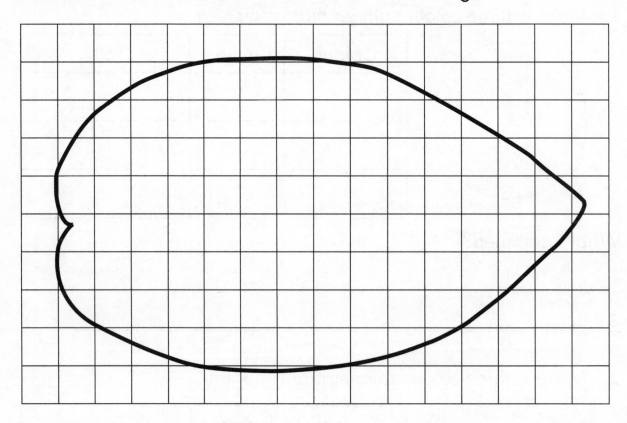

What to Measure	My Estimate	My Measure
length	_____ cm	_____ cm
width	_____ cm	_____ cm
distance around	_____ cm	_____ cm
space it covers	_____ squares	_____ squares

Find a leaf that will fit on the grid.
Trace around it.

Show your family all the different ways you can measure your leaf.
Record your measurements.

length: _____ cm   distance around: _____ cm

width: _____ cm   space it covers: _____ squares

🏠 **FAMILY NOTE:** Your child is learning to use measuring tools to measure irregular shapes. Please provide a ruler and some string or wool for measuring the distance around the leaf.

117

Measuring Area

Joey used the same length of string to form all the shapes below.

Count the squares covered by each shape.
Record in the chart.

A

B

C

D

E

F

Shape	A	B	C	D	E	F
number of squares covered						

What do you know about the distance around each shape?

_____

_____

Use a string to measure the distance around this rectangle.

Draw a different rectangle with the same distance around.

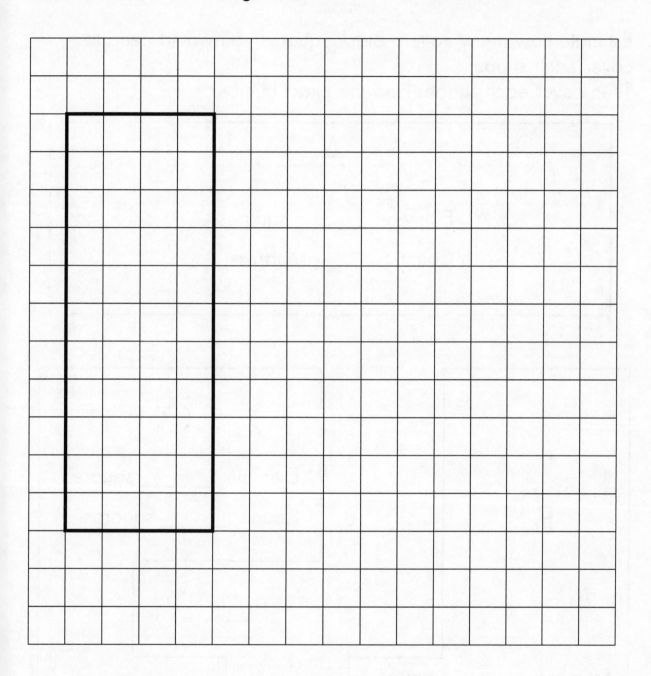

Count the number of squares each rectangle covers.
Write this number inside each rectangle.

Which rectangle covers more space? _____

_____

🏠 **FAMILY NOTE:** Your child has been learning about the relationship between area and perimeter. This activity will help your child see that figures with the same distance around can have different areas.

119

Measuring and Comparing Areas

Estimate how many Pattern Block squares you would need to cover each shape.
Then cover each shape. Find the exact number.

A

Estimate: _____ squares

Count: _____ squares

B

Estimate: _____ squares

Count: _____ squares

C

Estimate: _____ squares

Count: _____ squares

Which shape covers the most space? _____

Estimate how many grid squares each shape will cover.

Trace each shape and cut it out.
Place the tracing on the grid.
Count the squares.

Estimate: _____ squares

Count: _____ squares

Estimate: _____ squares

Count: _____ squares

Estimate: _____ squares

Count: _____ squares

FAMILY NOTE: Your child has been learning to measure area in square units. Help your child trace and cut out the shapes for this activity. Use thin or waxed paper so your child can see through the shapes to the grid squares below. Ask your child to explain how she or he arrives at an estimate.

Covering Area

Colour the large tile green.
Colour the small tile yellow.

Estimate how many large tiles will
cover the floor grid below. _____

Estimate how many small tiles will
cover the ceiling grid below. _____

Colour tiles to check.

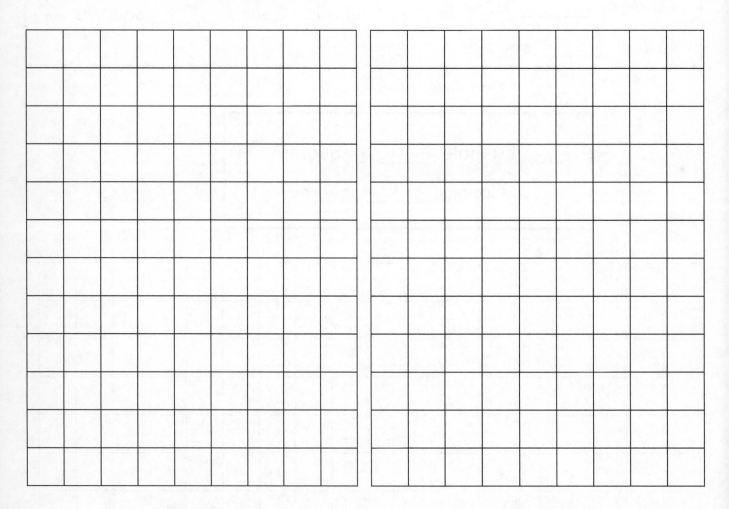

Floor

Ceiling

How many large tiles did it take?

How many small tiles did it take?

_____

_____

Ask a family member to help you
trace some copies of each tile.

Colour the large tiles one colour.
Colour the small tiles another colour.
Then cut out the tiles.

Cover this floor space. Use some large tiles and some small ones.
Try to make an interesting design.
Paste or tape the tiles in place.

Floor

Suppose the large tiles cost $10 and the small tiles cost $5.

How much would your floor cost? _____

🏠 **FAMILY NOTE:** Your child has been using paper tiles to explore the concept of area. Make about ten tiles of each size for this activity. Ask your child to try
several different arrangements before pasting down the tiles.

123

Exploring Equal Groups

Solve each problem.
Show your work.
Use pictures, numbers, and words.

How many wheels are on 4 tricycles?	How many toes are on 6 feet?
How many legs are on 5 cats?	How many ears are on 2 clowns?

124

Draw a creature from outer space.
Your creature should have 3 eyes, 2 mouths, and 4 horns.
Give your creature a name.

Name: _____

Suppose you saw 5 creatures like yours.
Use pictures and numbers to show what you would see.

How many eyes?	How many mouths?	How many horns?

FAMILY NOTE: Your child has been solving problems by putting together equal groups of objects. This is the first step in understanding multiplication as repeated addition. Ask your child to find items at home that represent equal groups, such as chairs with 4 legs or bicycles with 2 wheels. Have your child make up and solve problems about these items.

UNIT
11
ACTIVITY
2

Combining Equal Groups

Solve each problem.
Use pictures, numbers, and words.

How many legs are on 3 boys and 5 frogs?

How many legs are on 4 cows and 3 horses?

Make up a "How many legs?" problem about each pair of objects.
Solve each problem.
Use pictures, numbers, and words to show your work.

stools and chairs

spiders and ladybugs

FAMILY NOTE: Your child has been solving problems involving equal groups of two different sizes. Encourage your child to explain how she or he solved each problem.

Making Equal Groups

Find all the ways to divide 20 children into equal teams.
Use counters to help you.

Use pictures and numbers to show each way you find.

Play this game with a family member.
You will need 20 pennies or other small objects.
Spin a paper clip around a pencil point to work the spinner.

1. Spin the spinner.
Take that many pennies.

2. Divide the pennies into
equal groups so there are
none left over. Find three
different ways.

3. Record each way in the chart.
Take turns until the chart is done.
If you spin a number you've already
used, spin again.

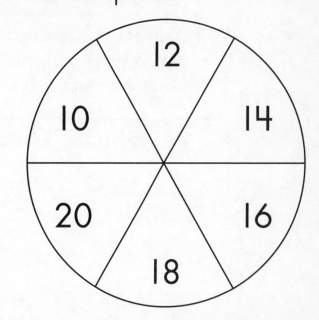

Player 1			
Round	Number I Spun	How Many in Each Group?	How Many Equal Groups?
1			
2			
3			

Player 2			
Round	Number I Spun	How Many in Each Group?	How Many Equal Groups?
1			
2			
3			

FAMILY NOTE: Your child is learning that some numbers can be divided into equal groups in different ways. For example, 14 can be divided into groups of 1, 2, 7, and 14. This game will help to reinforce this concept.

Sharing Sets Equally

Use counters. Solve each sharing problem.
Show your work with pictures, numbers, and words.
Tell if any counters are left over.

24 stickers for 8 children	14 pizza slices for 6 children
12 crayons for 3 children	15 apples for 5 children

Share each treat equally with your family.

How many people are in your family? _____

Draw pictures.
Show how many treats each person will get.
Show any treats that will be left over.

🏠 **FAMILY NOTE:** Your child is learning how to share sets equally among a given number of people. Ask what your child would do with any treats that are left over.

Computation
Skills
Bank

Addition Fact Strategies:
Counting On 1, 2, or 3

Strategy: When one of the numbers is 1, 2, or 3, start with the greater number and count on.

See: $7 + 2 =$ _____

Think: 7 ...8, 9

See: $3 + 9 =$ _____

Think: 9 ...10, 11, 12

$2 + 2 =$ ___	$6 + 1 =$ ___	$3 + 1 =$ ___
$2 + 9 =$ ___	$7 + 3 =$ ___	$5 + 1 =$ ___
$1 + 8 =$ ___	$7 + 1 =$ ___	$2 + 8 =$ ___
$4 + 3 =$ ___	$2 + 3 =$ ___	$7 + 2 =$ ___
$3 + 2 =$ ___	$2 + 1 =$ ___	$9 + 1 =$ ___
$4 + 1 =$ ___	$6 + 3 =$ ___	$2 + 4 =$ ___
$8 + 2 =$ ___	$8 + 1 =$ ___	$3 + 7 =$ ___

$$\begin{array}{cccccc} 2 & 5 & 2 & 7 & 4 & 8 \\ +4 & +2 & +9 & +2 & +1 & +3 \\ \hline \end{array}$$

$$\begin{array}{cccccc} 2 & 6 & 3 & 3 & 2 & 9 \\ +1 & +2 & +5 & +1 & +6 & +1 \\ \hline \end{array}$$

$$\begin{array}{cccccc} 9 & 7 & 2 & 5 & 3 & 6 \\ +3 & +1 & +5 & +1 & +8 & +1 \\ \hline \end{array}$$

FAMILY NOTE: Children should be encouraged to use thinking strategies that help them quickly determine the answers as they work toward mastery of basic facts. Please discuss with your child the strategy described in the box above. Help your child apply it as he or she completes the page.

Addition Fact Strategies: Turnarounds

Strategy: In addition, turnarounds have the same answer.

See: $9 + 2 =$ _____

Think: $2 + 9 = 11$, so $9 + 2 = 11$

Write the answer. Then write the turnaround.

$7 + 2 = 9$ $2 + 7 = 9$	$6 + 3 =$ __ _____
$1 + 7 =$ __ _____	$3 + 4 =$ __ _____
$6 + 2 =$ __ _____	$2 + 8 =$ __ _____
$5 + 1 =$ __ _____	$4 + 2 =$ __ _____
$1 + 4 =$ __ _____	$3 + 1 =$ __ _____
$5 + 2 =$ __ _____	$1 + 9 =$ __ _____
$3 + 8 =$ __ _____	$2 + 3 =$ __ _____
$9 + 2 =$ __ _____	$3 + 5 =$ __ _____
$1 + 6 =$ __ _____	$9 + 3 =$ __ _____
$3 + 7 =$ __ _____	$8 + 1 =$ __ _____
$1 + 2 =$ __ _____	$2 + 4 =$ __ _____

FAMILY NOTE: Children should be encouraged to use thinking strategies that help them quickly determine the answers as they work toward mastery of basic facts. Please discuss with your child the strategy described in the box above. Help your child apply it as he or she completes the page.

Addition Fact Strategies: Zero Facts

Strategy: When 0 is added to any number, the number stays the same.

See: 6 + 0 = _____   See: 0 + 9 = _____

Think: 6   Think: 9

5 + 0 = ___   7 + 0 = ___   0 + 5 = ___

0 + 9 = ___   0 + 6 = ___   1 + 0 = ___

2 + 0 = ___   4 + 0 = ___   6 + 0 = ___

0 + 1 = ___   9 + 0 = ___   0 + 8 = ___

6 + 0 = ___   0 + 3 = ___   5 + 0 = ___

2 + 0 = ___   4 + 0 = ___   0 + 8 = ___

0 + 6 = ___   0 + 7 = ___   7 + 0 = ___

$$\begin{array}{cccccc} 0 & 2 & 0 & 7 & 0 & 5 \\ +3 & +0 & +9 & +0 & +8 & +0 \\ \hline \end{array}$$

$$\begin{array}{cccccc} 6 & 0 & 9 & 0 & 4 & 0 \\ +0 & +3 & +0 & +8 & +0 & +1 \\ \hline \end{array}$$

FAMILY NOTE: Children should be encouraged to use thinking strategies that help them quickly determine the answers as they work toward mastery of basic facts. Please discuss with your child the strategy described in the box above. Help your child apply it as he or she completes the page.

Addition Fact Strategies: Choosing a Strategy (1)

$$\begin{array}{r} 4 \\ +3 \\ \hline \end{array} \qquad \begin{array}{r} 9 \\ +1 \\ \hline \end{array} \qquad \begin{array}{r} 2 \\ +5 \\ \hline \end{array} \qquad \begin{array}{r} 7 \\ +0 \\ \hline \end{array} \qquad \begin{array}{r} 7 \\ +1 \\ \hline \end{array} \qquad \begin{array}{r} 2 \\ +4 \\ \hline \end{array}$$

$$\begin{array}{r} 4 \\ +2 \\ \hline \end{array} \qquad \begin{array}{r} 2 \\ +6 \\ \hline \end{array} \qquad \begin{array}{r} 3 \\ +3 \\ \hline \end{array} \qquad \begin{array}{r} 1 \\ +8 \\ \hline \end{array} \qquad \begin{array}{r} 6 \\ +3 \\ \hline \end{array} \qquad \begin{array}{r} 8 \\ +0 \\ \hline \end{array}$$

$$\begin{array}{r} 3 \\ +9 \\ \hline \end{array} \qquad \begin{array}{r} 5 \\ +2 \\ \hline \end{array} \qquad \begin{array}{r} 0 \\ +2 \\ \hline \end{array} \qquad \begin{array}{r} 6 \\ +2 \\ \hline \end{array} \qquad \begin{array}{r} 9 \\ +0 \\ \hline \end{array} \qquad \begin{array}{r} 1 \\ +1 \\ \hline \end{array}$$

$$\begin{array}{r} 0 \\ +8 \\ \hline \end{array} \qquad \begin{array}{r} 3 \\ +4 \\ \hline \end{array} \qquad \begin{array}{r} 5 \\ +3 \\ \hline \end{array} \qquad \begin{array}{r} 0 \\ +7 \\ \hline \end{array} \qquad \begin{array}{r} 3 \\ +2 \\ \hline \end{array} \qquad \begin{array}{r} 3 \\ +7 \\ \hline \end{array}$$

3 + 8 = _____   0 + 6 = _____   8 + 3 = _____

1 + 5 = _____   3 + 7 = _____   2 + 7 = _____

2 + 9 = _____   6 + 3 = _____   8 + 2 = _____

6 + 1 = _____   2 + 8 = _____   3 + 2 = _____

7 + 2 = _____   4 + 1 = _____   0 + 4 = _____

5 + 3 = _____   9 + 0 = _____   3 + 9 = _____

1 + 3 = _____   9 + 2 = _____   0 + 1 = _____

FAMILY NOTE: Remind your child of the addition fact strategies introduced on previous pages. You may want to have your child find and answer all the facts on this page that fit each strategy, one at a time. For example, do all the "count on" and "turnaround" facts first, and then the "zero" facts.

Addition Fact Strategies: Doubles

 1 + 1    2 + 2    3 + 3    4 + 4    5 + 5   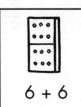 6 + 6

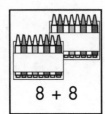 7 + 7    8 + 8   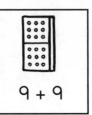 9 + 9

Strategy: When the numbers are the same, think of the picture.

See: 7 + 7 = _____   See: 8 + 8 = _____

Think: days in 2 weeks   Think: boxes of crayons

7 + 7 = ____   2 + 2 = ____   9 + 9 = ____

6 + 6 = ____   1 + 1 = ____   4 + 4 = ____

5 + 5 = ____   4 + 4 = ____   8 + 8 = ____

7 + 7 = ____   8 + 8 = ____   5 + 5 = ____

1 + 1 = ____   4 + 4 = ____   3 + 3 = ____

$$\begin{array}{r} 7 \\ +7 \\ \hline \end{array} \qquad \begin{array}{r} 9 \\ +9 \\ \hline \end{array} \qquad \begin{array}{r} 3 \\ +3 \\ \hline \end{array} \qquad \begin{array}{r} 6 \\ +6 \\ \hline \end{array} \qquad \begin{array}{r} 2 \\ +2 \\ \hline \end{array} \qquad \begin{array}{r} 8 \\ +8 \\ \hline \end{array}$$

FAMILY NOTE: Children should be encouraged to use thinking strategies that help them quickly determine the answers as they work toward mastery of basic facts. Please discuss with your child the strategy described in the box above. Help your child apply it as he or she completes the page.

Addition Fact Strategies:
Doubles Plus 1

Strategy: When one number is 1 more than the other number, think of the doubles picture and add 1.

See: $7 + 8 =$ _____   See: $4 + 5 =$ _____

Think: $7 + 7 = 14...15$ Think: $4 + 4 = 8...9$

$9 + 8 =$ _____ $3 + 2 =$ _____ $2 + 3 =$ _____

$7 + 8 =$ _____ $5 + 4 =$ _____ $7 + 6 =$ _____

$6 + 5 =$ _____ $6 + 7 =$ _____ $8 + 9 =$ _____

$3 + 4 =$ _____ $7 + 8 =$ _____ $4 + 5 =$ _____

$5 + 6 =$ _____ $8 + 7 =$ _____ $4 + 3 =$ _____

$7 + 6 =$ _____ $9 + 8 =$ _____ $8 + 7 =$ _____

$3 + 4 =$ _____ $5 + 4 =$ _____ $6 + 7 =$ _____

5	3	7	6	9	8
$+4$	$+4$	$+8$	$+5$	$+8$	$+7$

3	4	7	4	5	2
$+2$	$+5$	$+6$	$+3$	$+6$	$+3$

Addition Fact Strategies: Choosing a Strategy (2)

$$
\begin{array}{cccccc}
9 & 2 & 8 & 9 & 0 & 3 \\
+0 & +9 & +8 & +1 & +1 & +2 \\
\end{array}
$$

$$
\begin{array}{cccccc}
7 & 0 & 4 & 8 & 4 & 2 \\
+8 & +8 & +3 & +2 & +5 & +4 \\
\end{array}
$$

$$
\begin{array}{cccccc}
8 & 1 & 6 & 5 & 9 & 7 \\
+9 & +9 & +5 & +4 & +3 & +7 \\
\end{array}
$$

5 + 5 = ___	9 + 3 = ___	8 + 3 = ___
6 + 3 = ___	6 + 7 = ___	6 + 5 = ___
1 + 8 = ___	3 + 8 = ___	6 + 6 = ___
9 + 9 = ___	3 + 5 = ___	7 + 3 = ___
3 + 4 = ___	2 + 6 = ___	7 + 1 = ___
5 + 2 = ___	7 + 6 = ___	0 + 8 = ___
1 + 6 = ___	4 + 4 = ___	2 + 7 = ___
0 + 7 = ___	7 + 8 = ___	7 + 7 = ___
1 + 8 = ___	1 + 5 = ___	8 + 9 = ___

Addition Fact Strategies: Making 10

Strategy: When one of the numbers is 7, 8, or 9, make 10 and add the extras.

See: 7 + 4 = _____   See: 3 + 9 = _____

Think: 7 + 3 = 10   Think: 9 + 1 = 10

      10 + 1 = 11   10 + 2 = 12

9 + 8 = _____   8 + 4 = _____   9 + 4 = _____

3 + 9 = _____   9 + 5 = _____   8 + 7 = _____

7 + 9 = _____   2 + 9 = _____   7 + 6 = _____

8 + 9 = _____   8 + 9 = _____   6 + 8 = _____

6 + 9 = _____   8 + 5 = _____   8 + 3 = _____

7 + 8 = _____   9 + 7 = _____   4 + 9 = _____

7 + 4 = _____   7 + 5 = _____   4 + 7 = _____

$$\begin{array}{cccccc} 9 & 7 & 6 & 8 & 9 & 7 \\ +4 & +9 & +8 & +5 & +2 & +8 \end{array}$$

$$\begin{array}{cccccc} 8 & 9 & 7 & 3 & 9 & 6 \\ +4 & +5 & +5 & +9 & +7 & +9 \end{array}$$

FAMILY NOTE: Children should be encouraged to use thinking strategies that help them quickly determine the answers as they work toward mastery of basic facts. Please discuss with your child the strategy described in the box above. Help your child apply it as he or she completes the page.

Addition Fact Strategies: Almost Neighbours

Strategy: When the numbers are 2 apart on a number line, go to the middle number and double it.

See: 6 + 8 = _____

Think: Go to 7 and double.
7 + 7 = 14, so 6 + 8 = 14

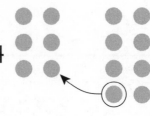

Move one counter from 8 to make 7 and 7.

1 + 3	9 + 7	6 + 8	3 + 5	5 + 7	4 + 6
7 + 9	3 + 1	2 + 4	7 + 5	6 + 8	9 + 7
5 + 3	7 + 9	8 + 6	4 + 2	6 + 4	2 + 4

9 + 7 = _____   5 + 7 = _____   6 + 4 = _____

4 + 6 = _____   5 + 3 = _____   2 + 4 = _____

7 + 5 = _____   8 + 6 = _____   6 + 8 = _____

5 + 3 = _____   1 + 3 = _____   5 + 7 = _____

🏠 **FAMILY NOTE:** Children should be encouraged to use thinking strategies that help them quickly determine the answers as they work toward mastery of basic facts. Please discuss with your child the strategy described in the box above. Help your child apply it as he or she completes the page.

Addition Fact Strategies: Choosing a Strategy (3)

9 + 7 = _____   3 + 5 = _____   9 + 5 = _____

4 + 2 = _____   9 + 2 = _____   7 + 9 = _____

4 + 6 = _____   7 + 8 = _____   8 + 9 = _____

7 + 6 = _____   8 + 6 = _____   9 + 6 = _____

6 + 9 = _____   3 + 1 = _____   3 + 9 = _____

7 + 5 = _____   9 + 7 = _____   7 + 9 = _____

8 + 7 = _____   7 + 7 = _____   6 + 0 = _____

1 + 7 = _____   4 + 3 = _____   0 + 9 = _____

4	3	7	4	7	4
+2	+9	+5	+6	+5	+9

8	8	6	3	8	9
+6	+9	+8	+5	+8	+5

9	9	9	8	9	7
+4	+9	+7	+5	+8	+6

FAMILY NOTE: Remind your child of the addition fact strategies introduced on previous pages. You may want to have your child find and answer all the facts on this page that fit each strategy, one at a time. For example, do all the "almost neighbours" facts first, and then the "making 10" facts.

Addition Facts: Sums to 10

5 + 5	3 + 4	9 + 0	4 + 5	6 + 2	6 + 4
5 + 3	2 + 5	2 + 3	8 + 2	2 + 6	5 + 4
8 + 1	3 + 5	6 + 1	4 + 2	6 + 3	0 + 9
3 + 6	9 + 1	1 + 5	4 + 3	7 + 1	7 + 3

6 + 4 = _____   2 + 7 = _____   8 + 2 = _____

3 + 3 = _____   8 + 0 = _____   8 + 1 = _____

7 + 2 = _____   7 + 3 = _____   4 + 4 = _____

9 + 1 = _____   7 + 1 = _____   2 + 5 = _____

4 + 2 = _____   1 + 5 = _____   4 + 1 = _____

6 + 1 = _____   2 + 3 = _____   1 + 3 = _____

1 + 4 = _____   0 + 5 = _____   0 + 2 = _____

Addition Facts: Sums to 12

9 + 3 = _____   4 + 6 = _____   4 + 7 = _____

7 + 4 = _____   4 + 8 = _____   7 + 3 = _____

2 + 8 = _____   1 + 9 = _____   5 + 5 = _____

9 + 1 = _____   8 + 1 = _____   0 + 9 = _____

5 + 7 = _____   6 + 5 = _____   5 + 4 = _____

2 + 7 = _____   3 + 6 = _____   1 + 8 = _____

8 + 4 = _____   7 + 2 = _____   2 + 6 = _____

5 + 6 = _____   6 + 4 = _____   5 + 3 = _____

4 + 5 = _____   3 + 5 = _____   7 + 1 = _____

5 + 2 = _____   2 + 4 = _____   3 + 4 = _____

6	2	7	9	2	8
+6	+8	+3	+3	+9	+3

3	4	5	9	3	2
+8	+4	+7	+2	+6	+6

Addition Facts: Sums to 15

6 + 8	0 + 2	4 + 7	9 + 4	6 + 6	9 + 5
5 + 8	8 + 7	3 + 4	3 + 7	9 + 2	6 + 5
7 + 5	4 + 6	6 + 7	9 + 6	5 + 6	5 + 7
4 + 8	8 + 6	3 + 5	8 + 2	5 + 9	9 + 3

2 + 9 = ___   6 + 7 = ___   9 + 4 = ___

8 + 7 = ___   4 + 7 = ___   4 + 8 = ___

9 + 3 = ___   8 + 2 = ___   9 + 2 = ___

7 + 7 = ___   9 + 6 = ___   3 + 8 = ___

6 + 3 = ___   5 + 4 = ___   2 + 5 = ___

5 + 8 = ___   3 + 3 = ___   5 + 0 = ___

8 + 3 = ___   0 + 0 = ___   1 + 3 = ___

Addition Facts: Sums to 18 (1)

7 + 8 = _____   6 + 8 = _____   8 + 9 = _____

5 + 9 = _____   9 + 4 = _____   6 + 9 = _____

5 + 7 = _____   6 + 7 = _____   9 + 2 = _____

5 + 8 = _____   4 + 8 = _____   8 + 2 = _____

9 + 9 = _____   8 + 7 = _____   9 + 3 = _____

8 + 3 = _____   4 + 7 = _____   7 + 4 = _____

6 + 4 = _____   2 + 9 = _____   9 + 1 = _____

8 + 4 = _____   8 + 5 = _____   7 + 5 = _____

0 + 8 = _____   2 + 2 = _____   1 + 7 = _____

6	6	7	8	6	7
+9	+6	+9	+3	+7	+7

8	6	8	9	9	5
+8	+5	+9	+3	+7	+6

5	2	6	3	3	9
+9	+6	+8	+7	+3	+4

Addition Facts: Sums to 18 (2)

5	9	9	3	5	7
+1	+2	+4	+8	+7	+2

3	9	5	9	1	4
+9	+5	+3	+3	+1	+2

9	5	7	2	4	2
+8	+6	+9	+5	+7	+3

4	9	0	8	1	6
+9	+8	+4	+2	+2	+1

9 + 8 = ___ 4 + 3 = ___ 7 + 1 = ___

2 + 0 = ___ 5 + 8 = ___ 6 + 2 = ___

7 + 9 = ___ 7 + 6 = ___ 4 + 7 = ___

9 + 9 = ___ 1 + 3 = ___ 4 + 4 = ___

4 + 1 = ___ 9 + 6 = ___ 8 + 6 = ___

8 + 1 = ___ 6 + 3 = ___ 6 + 9 = ___

7 + 8 = ___ 7 + 6 = ___ 5 + 4 = ___

Addition Facts: Sums to 18 (3)

3 + 3 = _____   1 + 2 = _____   2 + 5 = _____

1 + 7 = _____   3 + 4 = _____   8 + 4 = _____

0 + 1 = _____   3 + 6 = _____   4 + 2 = _____

3 + 8 = _____   9 + 2 = _____   3 + 7 = _____

2 + 3 = _____   1 + 8 = _____   2 + 2 = _____

4 + 6 = _____   5 + 6 = _____   5 + 3 = _____

4 + 8 = _____   8 + 3 = _____   6 + 8 = _____

2 + 6 = _____   6 + 7 = _____   1 + 4 = _____

3 + 1 = _____   7 + 7 = _____   7 + 2 = _____

8 + 7 = _____   9 + 9 = _____   8 + 8 = _____

$$\begin{array}{cccccc} 7 & 5 & 0 & 6 & 1 & 7 \\ +5 & +9 & +1 & +6 & +6 & +4 \end{array}$$

$$\begin{array}{cccccc} 5 & 5 & 4 & 2 & 1 & 9 \\ +4 & +8 & +7 & +0 & +5 & +1 \end{array}$$

Subtraction Fact Strategies: Counting Back 1, 2, or 3

Strategy: When subtracting 1, 2, or 3, start with the greater number and count back.

See: $10 - 2 =$ _____

Think: 10...9, 8

See: $11 - 3 =$ _____

Think: 11...10, 9, 8

$3 - 1 =$ _____

$2 - 2 =$ _____

$8 - 2 =$ _____

$4 - 3 =$ _____

$8 - 1 =$ _____

$5 - 1 =$ _____

$12 - 3 =$ _____

$3 - 3 =$ _____

$7 - 3 =$ _____

$3 - 2 =$ _____

$1 - 1 =$ _____

$10 - 3 =$ _____

$9 - 3 =$ _____

$7 - 2 =$ _____

$9 - 1 =$ _____

$6 - 1 =$ _____

$6 - 3 =$ _____

$4 - 2 =$ _____

$9 - 2 =$ _____

$4 - 1 =$ _____

$11 - 2 =$ _____

$11 - 3 =$ _____

$8 - 3 =$ _____

$9 - 3 =$ _____

$$\begin{array}{c}2\\-1\\\hline\end{array} \qquad \begin{array}{c}5\\-3\\\hline\end{array} \qquad \begin{array}{c}10\\-1\\\hline\end{array} \qquad \begin{array}{c}12\\-3\\\hline\end{array} \qquad \begin{array}{c}7\\-1\\\hline\end{array} \qquad \begin{array}{c}5\\-2\\\hline\end{array}$$

$$\begin{array}{c}10\\-3\\\hline\end{array} \qquad \begin{array}{c}6\\-2\\\hline\end{array} \qquad \begin{array}{c}7\\-3\\\hline\end{array} \qquad \begin{array}{c}10\\-2\\\hline\end{array} \qquad \begin{array}{c}8\\-3\\\hline\end{array} \qquad \begin{array}{c}11\\-3\\\hline\end{array}$$

Subtraction Fact Strategies: Zero Facts

> Strategy: When you take away all, 0 is left.
>
> See: $7 - 7 =$ _____   Think: Take away all, 0 is left.

$$
\begin{array}{ccccc}
9 & 5 & 6 & 1 & 2 & 4 \\
-9 & -5 & -6 & -1 & -2 & -4 \\
\hline
\end{array}
$$

$$
\begin{array}{cccccc}
5 & 2 & 3 & 8 & 1 & 7 \\
-5 & -2 & -3 & -8 & -1 & -7 \\
\hline
\end{array}
$$

$4 - 4 =$ _____ $9 - 9 =$ _____ $5 - 5 =$ _____

> Strategy: When you take away 0 from any number, the
>   number stays the same.
>
> See: $8 - 0 =$ _____   Think: Take away 0, leave all.

$3 - 0 =$ _____ $4 - 0 =$ _____ $2 - 0 =$ _____

$6 - 0 =$ _____ $8 - 0 =$ _____ $0 - 0 =$ _____

$1 - 0 =$ _____ $5 - 0 =$ _____ $9 - 0 =$ _____

$$
\begin{array}{cccccc}
4 & 8 & 7 & 6 & 9 & 3 \\
-0 & -0 & -0 & -0 & -0 & -0 \\
\hline
\end{array}
$$

FAMILY NOTE: Children should be encouraged to use thinking strategies that help them quickly determine the answers as they work toward mastery of basic facts. Please discuss with your child the strategies described in the boxes above. Help your child apply them as he or she completes the page.

Subtraction Fact Strategies: Choosing a Strategy (1)

8 − 0	11 − 3	5 − 5	1 − 1	6 − 0	2 − 2
1 − 0	7 − 0	4 − 3	10 − 3	3 − 2	4 − 4
4 − 2	12 − 3	2 − 1	9 − 9	11 − 2	0 − 0
2 − 0	5 − 3	6 − 1	9 − 3	5 − 0	10 − 1

3 – 1 = ___	6 – 2 = ___	5 – 1 = ___
9 – 1 = ___	3 – 3 = ___	7 – 2 = ___
5 – 2 = ___	6 – 6 = ___	10 – 2 = ___
6 – 3 = ___	4 – 1 = ___	7 – 3 = ___
8 – 3 = ___	8 – 2 = ___	7 – 7 = ___
8 – 8 = ___	4 – 0 = ___	3 – 0 = ___
9 – 2 = ___	7 – 1 = ___	8 – 1 = ___

FAMILY NOTE: Remind your child of the subtraction fact strategies introduced on previous pages. You may want to have your child find and answer all the facts on this page that fit each strategy, one at a time. For example, do all the "count back" facts first, then the "taking away all" facts, and finally the "taking away 0" facts.

152

Subtraction Fact Strategies: Doubles

 2 – 1    4 – 2   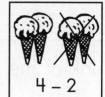 6 – 3   8 – 4    10 – 5   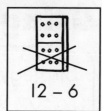 12 – 6

 14 – 7   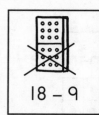 16 – 8   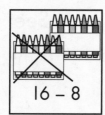 18 – 9

Strategy: When you subtract half of a number, think of
the doubles picture.

See: 14 – 7 = _____   Think: days in 2 weeks

```
  8        14         2         12        6        18
– 4       – 7       – 1       – 6       – 3       – 9


 16         4         12        10        18        16
– 8       – 2       – 6       – 5       – 9       – 8
```

16 – 8 = ____   2 – 1 = ____   10 – 5 = ____

14 – 7 = ____   10 – 5 = ____   18 – 9 = ____

4 – 2 = ____   12 – 6 = ____   16 – 8 = ____

18 – 9 = ____   8 – 4 = ____   12 – 6 = ____

153

Subtraction Fact Strategies: Using a Ten-Frame

Strategy: When subtracting from 9 or 10, think of the ten-frame.

See: 10 – 4 = _____   See: 9 – 4 = _____

Think: Fill the ten-frame.   Think: Put 9 in the ten-frame.

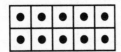   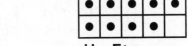

Take away 4. Six are left.   Take away 4. Five are left.

   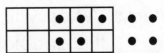

9 – 5 = _____   10 – 1 = _____   9 – 4 = _____

10 – 5 = _____   10 – 4 = _____   10 – 8 = _____

9 – 1 = _____   9 – 3 = _____   10 – 7 = _____

10 – 6 = _____   9 – 9 = _____   9 – 6 = _____

10 – 3 = _____   9 – 2 = _____   10 – 9 = _____

9 – 6 = _____   10 – 2 = _____   9 – 7 = _____

$$\begin{array}{cccccc} 10 & 9 & 10 & 9 & 9 & 9 \\ \underline{-\ 7} & \underline{-\ 3} & \underline{-\ 3} & \underline{-\ 1} & \underline{-\ 8} & \underline{-\ 5} \end{array}$$

$$\begin{array}{cccccc} 9 & 10 & 9 & 9 & 10 & 10 \\ \underline{-\ 7} & \underline{-\ 9} & \underline{-\ 8} & \underline{-\ 9} & \underline{-\ 2} & \underline{-\ 8} \end{array}$$

FAMILY NOTE: Children should be encouraged to use thinking strategies that help them quickly determine the answers as they work toward mastery of basic facts. Please discuss with your child the strategy described in the box above. Help your child apply it as he or she completes the page.

Subtraction Fact Strategies: Choosing a Strategy (2)

18 − 9 = _____   10 − 8 = _____   10 − 5 = _____

3 − 2 = _____   3 − 3 = _____   16 − 8 = _____

9 − 2 = _____   10 − 3 = _____   4 − 2 = _____

4 − 3 = _____   10 − 6 = _____   7 − 2 = _____

9 − 9 = _____   6 − 2 = _____   12 − 3 = _____

6 − 1 = _____   14 − 7 = _____   9 − 5 = _____

9 − 0 = _____   10 − 4 = _____   9 − 7 = _____

9 − 6 = _____   11 − 3 = _____   9 − 8 = _____

10	10	8	5	8	10
− 2	− 9	− 8	− 2	− 3	− 7

7	5	7	11	8	9
− 7	− 3	− 1	− 2	− 2	− 3

16	7	9	6	6	18
− 8	− 3	− 4	− 6	− 3	− 9

FAMILY NOTE: Remind your child of the subtraction fact strategies introduced on previous pages. You may want to have your child find and answer all the facts on this page that fit each strategy, one at a time. For example, do all the "count back" facts first, then the "taking away all" facts, the "taking away 0" facts, the "doubles" facts, and the "using a ten-frame" facts.

Subtraction Fact Strategies: Counting Up

Strategy: When the numbers are close neighbours, count up.

See: $11 - 9 =$ _____

Think: 9...10, 11 ———→ That's 2.

$11 - 8 =$ _____ $8 - 7 =$ _____ $8 - 5 =$ _____

$9 - 6 =$ _____ $6 - 5 =$ _____ $7 - 4 =$ _____

$6 - 4 =$ _____ $10 - 9 =$ _____ $6 - 3 =$ _____

$8 - 6 =$ _____ $9 - 7 =$ _____ $11 - 8 =$ _____

$7 - 5 =$ _____ $4 - 1 =$ _____ $10 - 8 =$ _____

$10 - 7 =$ _____ $12 - 9 =$ _____ $9 - 6 =$ _____

$11 - 9 =$ _____ $8 - 5 =$ _____ $7 - 4 =$ _____

8	10	9	12	9	5
− 6	− 7	− 7	− 9	− 8	− 2

11	7	5	10	4	10
− 9	− 6	− 3	− 9	− 2	− 8

7	5	8	4	9	7
− 6	− 4	− 7	− 3	− 8	− 5

🏠 **FAMILY NOTE:** Children should be encouraged to use thinking strategies that help them quickly determine the answers as they work toward mastery of basic facts. Please discuss with your child the strategy described in the box above. Help your child apply it as he or she completes the page.

Subtraction Fact Strategies: Think Addition

Strategy: When subtracting from a teen number, think of the related addition fact.

See: 13 – 8 = _____

Think: 8 + 5 = 13, so 13 – 8 = 5

12 – 8 = _____   11 – 4 = _____   14 – 8 = _____

14 – 7 = _____   13 – 9 = _____   12 – 3 = _____

16 – 7 = _____   12 – 7 = _____   14 – 9 = _____

13 – 8 = _____   14 – 5 = _____   15 – 7 = _____

14 – 6 = _____   15 – 8 = _____   16 – 9 = _____

13 – 7 = _____   17 – 8 = _____   15 – 7 = _____

15 – 6 = _____   18 – 9 = _____   14 – 8 = _____

11	12	15	13	12	17
– 6	– 6	– 9	– 5	– 4	– 9

11	13	11	16	13	12
– 5	– 6	– 7	– 8	– 4	– 5

FAMILY NOTE: Children should be encouraged to use thinking strategies that help them quickly determine the answers as they work toward mastery of basic facts. Please discuss with your child the strategy described in the box above. Help your child apply it as he or she completes the page.

Subtraction Fact Strategies: Choosing a Strategy (3)

12	11	13	11	12	15
− 6	− 9	− 8	− 8	− 5	− 6

13	17	12	13	9	12
− 7	− 8	− 7	− 9	− 8	− 4

15	12	16	12	13	10
− 9	− 9	− 9	− 8	− 6	− 9

14	15	11	18	14	15
− 9	− 8	− 7	− 9	− 5	− 7

$17 - 9 = \underline{\hspace{1cm}}$ $14 - 6 = \underline{\hspace{1cm}}$ $12 - 3 = \underline{\hspace{1cm}}$

$14 - 8 = \underline{\hspace{1cm}}$ $16 - 7 = \underline{\hspace{1cm}}$ $11 - 6 = \underline{\hspace{1cm}}$

$11 - 4 = \underline{\hspace{1cm}}$ $13 - 5 = \underline{\hspace{1cm}}$ $14 - 7 = \underline{\hspace{1cm}}$

$16 - 8 = \underline{\hspace{1cm}}$ $11 - 5 = \underline{\hspace{1cm}}$ $10 - 8 = \underline{\hspace{1cm}}$

$13 - 4 = \underline{\hspace{1cm}}$ $10 - 6 = \underline{\hspace{1cm}}$ $9 - 7 = \underline{\hspace{1cm}}$

$10 - 7 = \underline{\hspace{1cm}}$ $14 - 7 = \underline{\hspace{1cm}}$ $10 - 1 = \underline{\hspace{1cm}}$

$18 - 9 = \underline{\hspace{1cm}}$ $10 - 8 = \underline{\hspace{1cm}}$ $9 - 0 = \underline{\hspace{1cm}}$

FAMILY NOTE: Remind your child of the subtraction fact strategies introduced on previous pages. You may want to have your child find and answer all the facts on this page that fit each strategy, one at a time. For example, do all the "counting up" facts first, and then the "think addition" facts.

Subtraction Facts:
Subtracting from 1 to 10

10 – 7 = _____	10 – 6 = _____	8 – 6 = _____
6 – 3 = _____	9 – 1 = _____	1 – 1 = _____
7 – 5 = _____	5 – 4 = _____	4 – 3 = _____
9 – 4 = _____	6 – 4 = _____	9 – 2 = _____
3 – 2 = _____	7 – 4 = _____	6 – 0 = _____
10 – 2 = _____	2 – 1 = _____	10 – 5 = _____
8 – 5 = _____	9 – 7 = _____	7 – 6 = _____
9 – 5 = _____	8 – 4 = _____	9 – 8 = _____
6 – 5 = _____	10 – 9 = _____	8 – 3 = _____

$$
\begin{array}{cccccc}
1 & 7 & 10 & 5 & 9 & 10 \\
-1 & -2 & -8 & -2 & -3 & -4 \\
\hline
\end{array}
$$

$$
\begin{array}{cccccc}
9 & 4 & 8 & 6 & 7 & 8 \\
-6 & -1 & -8 & -2 & -7 & -2 \\
\hline
\end{array}
$$

$$
\begin{array}{cccccc}
7 & 5 & 8 & 8 & 4 & 10 \\
-3 & -3 & -7 & -1 & -2 & -3 \\
\hline
\end{array}
$$

Subtraction Facts: Subtracting from 1 to 12

11 − 7	5 − 3	11 − 6	8 − 3	4 − 3	10 − 4
7 − 4	11 − 5	6 − 3	10 − 5	7 − 5	11 − 8
9 − 3	8 − 4	11 − 4	12 − 8	5 − 2	12 − 6
10 − 8	2 − 2	12 − 9	10 − 6	9 − 2	6 − 4
3 − 2	7 − 3	12 − 5	11 − 3	12 − 7	7 − 2

$8 - 5 = \underline{\hspace{1cm}}$ $5 - 5 = \underline{\hspace{1cm}}$ $9 - 5 = \underline{\hspace{1cm}}$

$4 - 4 = \underline{\hspace{1cm}}$ $1 - 0 = \underline{\hspace{1cm}}$ $11 - 9 = \underline{\hspace{1cm}}$

$6 - 2 = \underline{\hspace{1cm}}$ $8 - 6 = \underline{\hspace{1cm}}$ $6 - 5 = \underline{\hspace{1cm}}$

$9 - 4 = \underline{\hspace{1cm}}$ $11 - 2 = \underline{\hspace{1cm}}$ $10 - 9 = \underline{\hspace{1cm}}$

$12 - 3 = \underline{\hspace{1cm}}$ $6 - 5 = \underline{\hspace{1cm}}$ $12 - 4 = \underline{\hspace{1cm}}$

Subtraction Facts:
Subtracting from 1 to 15

15 − 9 = ____   5 − 2 = ____   13 − 7 = ____

13 − 6 = ____   14 − 5 = ____   12 − 6 = ____

12 − 5 = ____   13 − 4 = ____   11 − 5 = ____

11 − 9 = ____   11 − 3 = ____   10 − 4 = ____

15 − 6 = ____   10 − 6 = ____   13 − 8 = ____

13 − 5 = ____   9 − 5 = ____   11 − 8 = ____

12 − 4 = ____   11 − 4 = ____   10 − 9 = ____

14 − 6 = ____   15 − 7 = ____   12 − 7 = ____

11 − 6 = ____   12 − 8 = ____   14 − 7 = ____

6 − 4 = ____   9 − 7 = ____   1 − 0 = ____

15	12	12	14	11	10
− 8	− 9	− 3	− 8	− 2	− 3

14	10	11	10	13	9
− 9	− 7	− 7	− 8	− 9	− 2

Subtraction Facts:
Subtracting from 1 to 18 (1)

| 8
− 3 | 16
− 9 | 14
− 7 | 11
− 4 | 17
− 8 | 3
− 2 |

| 11
− 5 | 14
− 8 | 9
− 4 | 12
− 3 | 7
− 5 | 11
− 2 |

| 12
− 4 | 11
− 3 | 4
− 2 | 13
− 4 | 14
− 6 | 16
− 8 |

| 2
− 1 | 15
− 9 | 13
− 9 | 14
− 5 | 16
− 7 | 15
− 8 |

| 6
− 2 | 13
− 5 | 9
− 7 | 13
− 8 | 11
− 7 | 10
− 6 |

11 − 9 = _____   1 − 1 = _____   15 − 6 = _____

10 − 5 = _____   11 − 6 = _____   5 − 3 = _____

13 − 7 = _____   12 − 5 = _____   13 − 6 = _____

14 − 9 = _____   11 − 8 = _____   17 − 9 = _____

12 − 6 = _____   15 − 7 = _____   18 − 9 = _____

Subtraction Facts:
Subtracting from 1 to 18 (2)

12 − 6 = _____   5 − 1 = _____   6 − 3 = _____

3 − 1 = _____   9 − 1 = _____   5 − 5 = _____

7 − 2 = _____   10 − 3 = _____   8 − 1 = _____

14 − 9 = _____   11 − 7 = _____   9 − 7 = _____

4 − 1 = _____   14 − 8 = _____   12 − 7 = _____

15 − 6 = _____   1 − 0 = _____   8 − 6 = _____

10 − 1 = _____   6 − 5 = _____   10 − 4 = _____

9 − 8 = _____   17 − 8 = _____   15 − 8 = _____

15 − 9 = _____   7 − 1 = _____   9 − 2 = _____

8 − 8 = _____   13 − 6 = _____   11 − 9 = _____

16 − 7 = _____   18 − 9 = _____   13 − 9 = _____

```
  12        8         5         9        14         4
−  5      − 2       − 4       − 6      −  5       − 4
____      ____      ____      ____      ____      ____

   8       13        10        11         6        11
− 4       − 7       − 5       − 8       − 4       − 6
____      ____      ____      ____      ____      ____
```

Subtraction Facts:
Subtracting from 1 to 18 (3)

7	10	8	4	9	3
− 4	− 1	− 5	− 2	− 3	− 3

11	6	11	10	7	5
− 3	− 1	− 2	− 6	− 3	− 2

10	12	13	2	11	12
− 7	− 3	− 5	− 1	− 4	− 8

7	9	6	8	12	10
− 7	− 4	− 3	− 3	− 9	− 9

14 − 7 = _____   13 − 4 = _____   7 − 6 = _____

18 − 9 = _____   3 − 2 = _____   16 − 8 = _____

10 − 8 = _____   6 − 2 = _____   9 − 5 = _____

13 − 8 = _____   10 − 2 = _____   11 − 5 = _____

2 − 2 = _____   5 − 3 = _____   12 − 4 = _____

14 − 6 = _____   7 − 5 = _____   13 − 9 = _____

15 − 7 = _____   16 − 9 = _____   17 − 9 = _____

Strategies for Adding Larger Numbers

There are many ways to add large numbers.
Here are some ways to add 27 and 48.

$$\begin{array}{r} 27 \\ + 48 \end{array}$$

1.

$20 + 40 = 60$	First add the tens.
$7 + 8 \quad = 15$	Then add the ones.
$60 + 15 = 75$	Then add the tens and ones.

2.

27 is 3 less than 30.

48 is 2 less than 50.

The answer must be 5 less than $30 + 50$ or 80.

$80 - 5 = 75$

3.

Take 2 from 27 and add it to 48.

$27 - 2 = 25$

$48 + 2 = 50$

$25 + 50 = 75$

4.

Add the ones. ⟶	Trade 10 ones ⟶ for 1 ten.	Add the tens.
$\begin{array}{r} 27 \\ + 48 \\ \hline \end{array}$ 15 ones	$\begin{array}{r} 1 \\ 27 \\ + 48 \\ \hline 5 \end{array}$	$\begin{array}{r} 1 \\ 27 \\ + 48 \\ \hline 75 \end{array}$

Addition: Larger Numbers (1)

25 + 43	60 + 32	76 + 21	14 + 15
23 + 16	53 + 42	21 + 44	13 + 42
75 + 13	32 + 32	43 + 35	26 + 71
42 + 35	70 + 20	34 + 42	17 + 12
63 + 24	11 + 43	32 + 45	35 + 44
47 + 21	36 + 3	23 + 54	38 + 31

Addition: Larger Numbers (2)

34 + 58	62 + 19	27 + 37	15 + 8
62 + 18	19 + 19	48 + 33	26 + 37
37 + 48	46 + 38	25 + 55	63 + 19
76 + 14	83 + 19	54 + 9	13 + 19
48 + 36	53 + 49	26 + 57	18 + 48
15 + 77	36 + 27	76 + 8	64 + 29

Addition: Larger Numbers (3)

37 + 41	56 + 39	25 + 7	16 + 12
29 + 54	40 + 37	62 + 53	85 + 19
63 + 34	57 + 3	25 + 25	71 + 15
26 + 49	33 + 43	13 + 42	31 + 59
62 + 35	47 + 38	39 + 6	34 + 59
26 + 43	35 + 58	48 + 48	18 + 47

Strategies for Subtracting Larger Numbers

There are many ways to subtract large numbers.
Here are some ways to subtract 39 from 87.

$$87 - 39$$

1. Count up in steps from 39 to 87.

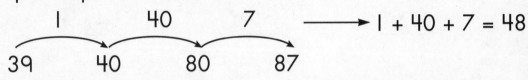

$$1 + 40 + 7 = 48$$

2. Subtract two simpler numbers that are the same distance apart.

Add 3 to 87 to make 90.
Add 3 to 39 to make 42.

To subtract 90 – 42, think: 90 – 40 – 2

50 – 2

48

3.
| Subtract 30 from 87: | 87 – 30 = 57 |
| Subtract 9 from 57: | 57 – 9 = 48 |

4.
| Subtract 40 from 87: | 87 – 40 = 47 |
| Add the extra 1: | 47 + 1 = 48 |

5.

We need more ones. ⟶ Trade 1 ten for 10 ones. ⟶ Subtract the ones. ⟶ Subtract the tens.

$$\begin{array}{r} 87 \\ -39 \\ \hline \end{array} \qquad \begin{array}{r} ^{7\ 17}\!\!\cancel{87} \\ -39 \\ \hline \end{array} \qquad \begin{array}{r} ^{7\ 17}\!\!\cancel{87} \\ -39 \\ \hline 8 \end{array} \qquad \begin{array}{r} ^{7\ 17}\!\!\cancel{87} \\ -39 \\ \hline 48 \end{array}$$

Subtraction: Larger Numbers (1)

$$
\begin{array}{r} 48 \\ -\,25 \\ \hline \end{array}
\qquad
\begin{array}{r} 67 \\ -\,43 \\ \hline \end{array}
\qquad
\begin{array}{r} 54 \\ -\,21 \\ \hline \end{array}
\qquad
\begin{array}{r} 39 \\ -\,16 \\ \hline \end{array}
$$

$$
\begin{array}{r} 92 \\ -\,51 \\ \hline \end{array}
\qquad
\begin{array}{r} 83 \\ -\,40 \\ \hline \end{array}
\qquad
\begin{array}{r} 55 \\ -\,4 \\ \hline \end{array}
\qquad
\begin{array}{r} 26 \\ -\,12 \\ \hline \end{array}
$$

$$
\begin{array}{r} 56 \\ -\,35 \\ \hline \end{array}
\qquad
\begin{array}{r} 45 \\ -\,22 \\ \hline \end{array}
\qquad
\begin{array}{r} 74 \\ -\,51 \\ \hline \end{array}
\qquad
\begin{array}{r} 83 \\ -\,50 \\ \hline \end{array}
$$

$$
\begin{array}{r} 22 \\ -\,11 \\ \hline \end{array}
\qquad
\begin{array}{r} 98 \\ -\,92 \\ \hline \end{array}
\qquad
\begin{array}{r} 33 \\ -\,31 \\ \hline \end{array}
\qquad
\begin{array}{r} 99 \\ -\,84 \\ \hline \end{array}
$$

$$
\begin{array}{r} 57 \\ -\,37 \\ \hline \end{array}
\qquad
\begin{array}{r} 86 \\ -\,42 \\ \hline \end{array}
\qquad
\begin{array}{r} 45 \\ -\,21 \\ \hline \end{array}
\qquad
\begin{array}{r} 39 \\ -\,16 \\ \hline \end{array}
$$

$$
\begin{array}{r} 68 \\ -\,25 \\ \hline \end{array}
\qquad
\begin{array}{r} 37 \\ -\,16 \\ \hline \end{array}
\qquad
\begin{array}{r} 96 \\ -\,43 \\ \hline \end{array}
\qquad
\begin{array}{r} 84 \\ -\,72 \\ \hline \end{array}
$$